A Candlelight Ecstasy Romance ™

HIS BODY WAS ALL MALE. . . .

. . . sending a telltale tingle through her. Remembrance of the touch of his lips on hers deepened that tingle to a shudder he could not have missed, bent intimately around her as he was. When the hand behind curved around her neck and he straightened, drawing her toward him, she went willingly. Earlier his kiss had been one of reacquaintance; now there was pure hunger in it. . . .

CANDLELIGHT ECSTASY ROMANCES™

WHISPERED PROMISE

Bonnie Drake

A CANDLELIGHT ECSTASY ROMANCE™

Published by
Dell Publishing Co., Inc.
1 Dag Hammarskjold Plaza
New York, New York 10017

Dell ® TM 681510, Dell Publishing Co., Inc.

Candlelight Ecstasy Romance™ is a trademark of Dell
Publishing Co., Inc., New York, New York.

ISBN: 0-440-17673-5

Printed in the United States of America

First printing—July 1982

Dear Reader:

In response to your continued enthusiasm for Candlelight Ecstasy Romances™, we are increasing the number of new titles from four to six per month.

We are delighted to present sensuous novels set in America, depicting modern American men and women as they confront the provocative problems of modern relationships.

Throughout the history of the Candlelight line, Dell has tried to maintain a high standard of excellence, to give you the finest in reading enjoyment. That is now and will remain our most ardent ambition.

Anne Gisonny
Editor
Candlelight Romances

To A.C.D., my second born

CHAPTER 1

For long moments the tall figure stood immobile behind the desk, palms flat on either side of the pile of press clippings. Deep in thought, he read the topmost item for the third time. Lost to him was the simple splendor of the office, with its rich mahogany desk and credenza, its robust leather armchairs, its long conference table, and numerous and stuffed bookshelves, as was the stately grandfather clock which slowly ticked off the minutes. The mass of photographs, political and personal alike, which covered the white walls looked with benign indulgence upon the sandy-colored head bent intently over the fresh newsprint.

Straightening to his full height, he was once more in command. The distance to the door diminished rapidly with several broad strides; a bronzed hand on the knob drew it quickly open. "Hollings!" The deep voice issued its command before its vibrant owner returned once more to his desk, leaving the door ajar. His steel-gray eyes were back on the same clipping when the shutting door announced the arrival of his aide.

"John, who in the devil is this Dr. Patterson?" The back of his hand rapped the top of the pile of press clippings as he raised his eyes to challenge his administrative assistant. Preliminaries were an unnecessary and ill-afforded luxury in their line of work. John Hollings was his right-hand man precisely because he understood this and always managed to be one step ahead.

Directly, the man opposite responded. "Somewhat of an enigma, Drew. A newcomer. Only in the state since last fall. Teaches child psychology at Trinity. On the side, executive director of the Connecticut Child Advocacy Project."

"For a newcomer, the name Patterson has established itself already," Drew commented. He straightened again and thrust both hands in the pockets of his gray gabardine slacks. "This is the second article in as many days, the fourth or fifth in the past few weeks. Dr. Patterson has become quite a spokesman."

"Spokeswoman," the aide corrected, a slow smile drawing at the corners of his mouth.

It was mirrored instantly as Drew Charles eased his tall frame into the high-backed leather chair behind him. "I stand corrected. And she has some tongue. Seems to feel that our bill falls far short. It's obvious that she's never been to Washington." His tongue-in-cheek quip, accompanied by a brief glance heavenward, was not lost on John Hollings.

"No doubt. We knew we were facing tough opposition when we first introduced this legislation, Drew, but this type of thing we didn't quite anticipate. And from home, no less!"

Again, the gray eyes fell across the newsprint. *"The Hartford Courant* is bad enough. It's the most widely read paper in the state. But at the rate she's going, it may be *The New York Times* next or, Lord help us, the *Washington Post."* The strong lips thinned to a frown as the finely honed mind moved ahead. "Find out everything you can on her, John. Let's know exactly what we're up against. And keep a close watch on possible developments. I don't want to risk anything before the bill is even sent to committee."

The swivel chair turned away from the aide, effectively dismissing him, as its occupant cast a pensive eye out the window. April in Washington was a sight to see, the famed cherry blossoms budding in pale pink harmony with the green buds on the trees and the revived growth of the lush-grassed malls. Spring had arrived, and with it the annual flow of visitors, heavy year round to this, the nation's capital, but particularly noticeable at the time of nature's rebirth. Legislators came and went, as did presidents, their aides, staffs, and families. Yet the bounty of the land remained, year after year, to live through its four-season cycle, then begin all over again.

In a brief idle moment, Drew Charles let his mind drift northward to his own Connecticut retreat. Spring would be several weeks behind there, with but the earliest green buds just beginning to emerge over the low hillside on which his home was hidden. It had been a month since he'd been there; that would have to be remedied. As it was, he was due to return the weekend after next, though the schedule of appearances which his press secretary, Dwight Dewhurst, had lined up offered little promise of the quiet time he wanted.

A sigh of resignation punctuated his thoughts as he once more thanked fate and his own determination that he had neither a wife nor children to neglect. For everything his job offered—and he found it to be the most stimulating thing, by far, that he had ever done in his life—it made a travesty of family life. With the inescapable bitterness that hounded him, his thoughts turned to his parents, then, as suddenly, mellowed. All alone now, his father had made the sacrifice and suffered for it daily. Drew vowed to make the time to spend with him, however short, when he returned home. After all, his father had no one else left to call family. No one else, but his son, the senator.

A fresh clipping stared starkly up from the desk top three days later. Again, there were long moments of concentration as gray eyes, slate-hard, studied it. Again there was a statuesque pose in the tall, well-muscled form above it. Again there was a terse summons for the administrative assistant.

"What more have you got, John?" he asked bluntly, settling back in his chair. It had been an exhausting few days of committee hearings, floor discussions, and several roll-call votes, all spiced with the informal conversations he had held with various of his colleagues by way of sampling the sentiment toward his newly proposed legislation. It was his baby, the Rights of Minors Act, and he was determined that it should flourish from inception to enactment. After ten years in Washington, the ins and outs of politics were clear to Drew. Understanding the process, however, was a far cry from exercising it. But he was on his way with this one, slowly and steadily, observing every unwritten word of protocol. It would be a long fight, one charged with emotion. Control, in its every intricate aspect, would be a determining factor. It was therefore critical that he identify and understand his opposition.

John Hollings deposited a manila folder on his boss's desk before taking a seat to the right. "Her qualifications appear to be legitimate enough. She's originally from Cleveland, has an M.A. and a Ph.D. from the University of Minnesota in child psychology. There's no record of any particular activism while she was a student there, or during the following years when she worked at a mental health center in San Francisco. Her doctoral dissertation —you have a summary of it there—" he gestured toward the folder "—seems to have made its mark, though. After

14

an intensive study of child custody disputes, both in Minnesota and in California, she suggested that, despite the good intentions of the courts, the best interests of the children, in a large number of cases, were simply not being served. Her hypothesis is backed up forcefully with a whole army of statistics. She makes a convincing argument."

A wry smile twisted the senator's lips. "I'm sure. Her arguments—and the way she states them—are potent in the clippings you've given me. She has a definite knack for words. If, as you suggest, she is an authority in the field—" the grind of the wheels in his mind were almost audible as his left forefinger stoked a clean-shaven cheek—"and she has the facts and figures to back up her arguments . . ." His words trailed off as his thoughts digressed slightly. "What about *her?*"

The question had been expected, and John Hollings was prepared. "Lives very quietly and alone in . . . get this," he added with a knowing grin, "Simsbury."

Drew got it; they were townsmates. "No family at all with her?"

"Appears not."

"What else?"

"She is well thought of in the area, according to our man Morrow in the Hartford office. People who meet her seem to like her. But she's all business. Keeps strictly to herself socially."

A tawny brow arched into the tanned forehead to scatter ripples beneath a fallen swath of hair. "How old?"

Amusement was subtly held in check as John answered. "Twenty-nine, several months short of the big three-oh." Having known Drew Charles since his first days in Washington, the aide could well imagine what was going through the senator's mind at that moment. Though he had never married, Drew had a distinct way with women.

15

He was able to hold them at arm's length as he wrapped them helplessly around his little finger. If his even, white smile didn't do it, there was always the effect of his lean and muscular physique or the magnetism of his eyes—business to bedroom in one blink, a smitten companion of John's had, to his own consternation, once aptly described them—or his renowned bachelor status itself. But no notorious playboy was this senator. His liaisons, in love as in politics, were well chosen, discreetly pursued, and succinctly carried out. This man was male through and through. Without doubt there had been many an evening spent incommunicado. And, if he was as good a lover as he was a brilliant thinker, any woman he chose to dally with would long remember him.

The brief silence was broken by Drew's soft laughter. "Feeling her oats as she crests the hill. Getting better, as they say." Then he paused, growing entirely serious. "Any photos of her?"

John merely smiled. "Sorry, chum. Nothing. She hasn't made the evening news yet. You'll just have to wait until you meet her."

The senator's rejoinder came as no surprise to his good friend. "I want you to call her, John. Invite her down for a day or two—at our expense, of course, as a potential resource for the hearings. I'd like a chance to talk with her. She may be able to help us, if we can win her over." The "we" was merely a figure of speech; both men knew that, in the end, it was Drew's job.

"Right." For now, that particular subject was over. "By the way, Senator Sharp's office phoned to say that he'd like you to sit in on the budget hearings. They're scheduled for eleven."

Half-turning, the senator withdrew a small 3-by-5 card from the inside pocket of his tan suit jacket, which hung over the back of the chair. "I can manage it for a few

16

minutes. I'm leaving soon to meet with the municipal leaders from Fairfield County, then there's that briefing for the trip to Central America, but—" he scrawled the time of the extra meeting between the lines of the jammed schedule card "—I'll be there. Henry Sharp is not one to be snubbed. We need his support." Sliding the card back into his jacket, he picked up the phone to return the first of the several calls which time would allow. John Hollings quietly left the room.

The matter of the vocal Dr. Patterson was not brought up again until two days later as the senator and his administrative assistant strode side by side down one of the long Capitol corridors following a roll-call vote on the Senate floor. It had been a minor issue, but one which Drew had supported strongly—an amendment to the military-procurement bill for the year. Satisfaction that the amendment had carried buoyed him; it was this very elation that made the job as rewarding as it was. Yet there was always a new battle to be waged.

"What about the child psychologist, John? Were you able to reach her?" Neither man's step faltered as they talked. It was commonplace, this communication-in-transit, the only drawback being the frequent greetings of passing legislators or the never-ending interruptions of visiting constituents, other aides, or the press. On this particular day, with a major hearing commencing in the Senate Caucus Room to which most attention had turned following the floor vote, the corridor was somewhat less congested.

John grimaced. "It took awhile, but I finally got through. She says to thank you for the invitation, but that she is busy." His tone was blunt, as were the words themselves, though his eyes held a certain expectancy as they watched for his boss's response.

17

"Busy?" Surprise brought Drew to a momentary halt, then, with a faint headshake, he regained his pace, deftly dodging a group of oncoming tourists who, mercifully, failed to recognize this, one of the younger and more dazzling members of the Senate. *Busy* . . . he thought, a puzzled expression on his face. It had been his experience, even during the years that he served as a representative in the House, that the average American would never pass up such an invitation to come to Washington. If it weren't the excitement of the town which lured him, it was the honor of taking part in the governmental process, even in the most indirect way. Dr. Patterson had given an outright refusal. And, knowing John Hollings as he did, every attempt had been made to twist her arm!

A corner was rounded to the chorus of several "Hey, Drew!"'s, each of which was returned by name. Then the two headed for the stairwell. John had long since learned that this brisk movement from appointment to appointment was a source of exercise for Drew, who typically avoided elevators—even with top priority given to members of the Senate brotherhood—whenever possible for that same reason. Now his concentration was in part devoted to keeping up the pace.

"How did she come across on the phone, John? Reasonable? Flexible? Receptive?"

For the first time, his aide appeared to hesitate. "It's strange. I can usually get a handle on someone through a phone conversation. But not this time. She seemed poised and intelligent, soft-spoken yet deliberate. She insisted— very politely—that her own schedule was nearly impossible, and that she just couldn't come so close to the end of the semester. I almost sensed that it was Washington she didn't want—that it had nothing to do with you or the bill."

Drew glanced quickly at the bemusement on his friend's

face, then let the subject temporarily drop as they arrived at the suite of offices of the junior senator from Connecticut. There were nods and smiles from Drew to his staff as he passed the open-doored offices of legislative assistants, research aides, press coordinators, and secretaries, en route to the farthermost of the offices, his own sanctum. Only there did he turn to face John, who had followed him in.

"Call her again, John." Determination was written all over the suntanned features. It was as though, in her own insistent way, Dr. Daran Patterson had thrown down the gauntlet. And Drew Charles, born competitor that he was, would not ignore it. "Set up a meeting for the weekend I'm to be home."

"But your schedule—" John began in protest, only to be silenced by Drew's own sigh, as the latter combed his fingers wearily through his casually groomed hair.

"I know, I know. And I've got to find some time, somewhere along the line, to spend with Dad. But this is important—I can sense it. She could be an important ally."

The skepticism that came and went in John Hollings's eye remained in his voice. "Is that the only reason? Or is curiosity getting the better of you? After all, it isn't every day that a lady turns down the illustrious Senator Andrew S. Charles."

It was a gentle teasing, from one friend to another, totally devoid of harshness, sarcasm, or jealousy. Drew acknowledged his friend's perceptivity with a sheepish grin. "You may be right, pal. But indulge me and set it up anyway," he ordered warmly, then raised his voice to signal a change in subject. "And get in touch with that feisty senator from Oklahoma with whom I'm supposed to be cosponsoring the alternative energy piece. We'd better get on the stick with that one—it's critical."

19

His administrative assistant smiled. "Isn't everything?" he asked rhetorically, then left.

Shucking his jacket and tossing it more carelessly than usual onto one of the plush leather chairs, the senator turned to the pile of letters on his desk, pushing from mind the conjured image of a plain and staid, monotonously self-righteous crusader for the children of Connecticut.

"Ah, let me see," the slender young woman hedged, tucking a long, dark wave absently behind a small gold-hoop-earringed ear. The refusal to journey to Washington had been simple and honest enough. Though it might have been arranged, a two- or even one-day absence, with exams fresh on the horizon, would have been difficult. But to spare at most an hour, and in the convenience of her own office no less, how could she decline the opportunity? This senator was certainly unusually accommodating; he had to have a motive. Perhaps her press attention was finally getting to him. *Well, it should.* His proposed bill was much too weak. If Washington was finally going to do something about the rights of minors in its domain, it ought to do it right. And, as she seemed to have become the local spokesperson for the cause, it would be irresponsible of her to squander this opportunity to communicate with the powers-that-be.

"Yes, noon would be fine, Mr. Hollings." There was a pause as she listened to the apologies of the senator's aide. "No, don't worry about it. I have appointments in the morning anyway. Lunch is not important." After another pause, she nodded. "Yes. My office then?" The traditional pleasantries of farewell followed before she replaced the receiver on its hook. Only then did she realize what she had let herself in for. This aide was a smooth one, his friendly banter temporarily taking her mind from her pre-set aversion to his line of work. Contact with Washington

20

was the last thing she wanted from the personal stand-point, yet it was an unavoidable necessity professionally. In terms of the Child Advocacy Project, of which she was the director, access to Senator Andrew Charles and his proposed legislation was critical. It had been fortuitous that the impetus for this long-evaded issue should come from the home-state senator. But, aside from the merits or demerits of the bill, this particular senator would be an experience in and of himself. The image of the man was well known countrywide. He was a tough and dedicated politician, smooth and silky. *Aren't they all,* she mused wryly, *when it suits them?* This particular senator was straightforward and hard-headed on matters he believed in. If his press was to be believed, the Rights of Minors Act was a cause from his heart. Though, technically, they were on the same side of the issue, there was plenty to argue about regarding specifics. She would have to be on her toes with this man, who was, no doubt, used to women falling all over him. The senator would have a rude awakening when he discovered that Daran Patterson was not his usual fawning fan. It had been a hard road, and one fraught with trial and error that she had traveled, but by now she hoped to effectively handle any good-looking, egotistical, basically ruthless—how overused that word, yet true, she thought—political star.

The shrill ring of her phone softened the scowl she had unknowingly donned. "Dr. Patterson speaking." At home a simple hello would have sufficed. Here, in the office, the greater formality was expected and appropriate.

"Daran? It's Glen. The switchboard said you were on long distance from Washington. Was it Charles's office?" Excitement ran high in the attorney's voice, coaxing a smile to Daran's oval-shaped face.

"The way the senator's aides announce him all over the place," she quipped with easy sarcasm, "you'd think he was up for reelection *this* November. They never miss a chance to win a vote. Hmm, I wonder what they promised the operator," she prattled on, her mockery now blatant. "Probably a signed picture of HIM, or, at least, a personalized letter of appreciation for plugging through the call."

"Daran, Daran, Daran," the male voice retorted amicably, "do you mean to say you *didn't* vote for him?"

"I didn't *live* here then, so I was spared the choice," she declared with an exaggerated sigh of relief. "How are you doing, Glen?" The subject was detoured for but an instant, until a breath of impatience returned it to its crux.

"Daran—" the warning note was suffused in his use of her name once again "—was it Senator Charles?"

As comfortable as was her relationship with Glen Roberts, as close as they had grown during the six months she had served as executive director to his managing attorney of the Connecticut Child Advocacy Project, Daran knew when he wanted a straight answer.

"Yes, it was. He's returning to the state next weekend. I have a meeting with him here at noon on Saturday."

"Fantastic! You must have really gotten through with those interviews the papers printed. A personal audience with the man himself. Not bad!"

For some strange reason Daran did not share her friend's wholehearted enthusiasm. As beneficial as it might prove to be, she was not looking forward to this meeting. "I suppose not," she finally mustered up. "But don't get your hopes up, Glen. He may give our project some publicity and a boost, but I doubt he'll let us seriously affect his bill. Actually he probably hopes to mollify us, to silence any opposition to his work. I'm sure it's just a token visit." Her skepticism, unusual in this customarily optimistic professional, was immediately noted by her coworker.

22

"Why so down on it all of a sudden? Haven't you been the one talking right and left about how little his legislation fits the realistic needs of minors? This is your chance; you'll have his undivided attention. If anyone can convince him, you can. After all—" his voice softened, teasing her with the knowledge of personal experience "—all you have to do is bat those lovely amber eyes of yours and smile a bit, and you'll have him in your pocket."

"Hmmph! From what I hear, he's apt to do just that to me. Have you ever met him, Glen?"

The voice at the other end of the line held no hesitancy. "Yes. I've run across him several times at one affair or another. Let me warn you—he is an impressive fellow. Makes eye contact constantly. Knows all the right words and motions and reactions."

Daran laughed, a harsh sound, out of character with its cynical undertone. "Don't they all! Those politicians are a breed unto themselves. They have such power at their disposal, yet . . ." Realizing the extent of her own overly personal response, she let her words fall by the wayside.

"Is something wrong, Daran? You sound unusually dismal. What is it?" Leave it to Glen to be so perceptive, Daran thought.

Grasping the telephone receiver tensely, she sought to quell his curiosity. "Oh, nothing. I guess I'm just skeptical. This is all happening so quickly. And it's a bad time for me here at school. Once the semester is over, I'll be able to think clearly again." If only it were true! In fact, it was only this headlong immersion into both teaching and the Project that had been her salvation. Running to San Francisco had solved nothing. Oh, yes, there had been new faces and fresh scenery, but the hurt had lingered. Time had passed since, however, and the ache had eased. Life in Connecticut was treating her well.

"Say, Daran, why not join us for dinner tonight?"

"Thanks, Glen, but—"

"Why not?" Glen was at his most direct best. But then, that was one of his traits she so admired, second to his sharp legal mind and his uncanny sense of perception.

"You know me, Glen. I really hate the public life—"

"What public life?" he interrupted with gentle rebuke. "This is just Lois and me. Come on. We're going to that new Italian place at the Civic Center. You'll like it," he coaxed persistently, knowing all too well that his efforts would be in vain.

"Thanks, really, but maybe another time."

Several seconds' silence dragged along the line. Carefully choosing his words, Glen finally spoke. "Daran, I'm not really sure what happened to you before you came here, but I do know that you've got to get out if you're ever going to get over it. You are a beautiful woman. You could have dates every night—"

"Glen—"

"No, hon, listen. I love you and so does Lois. We worry about you. Why do you isolate yourself from everyone?"

In an unobservable gesture of defense, her chin tilted upward slightly, as she rebutted his claim. "I don't isolate myself. There are people running in and out of here every day. I go to meetings and conferences and the hospital—"

"That's not what I'm talking about, and you know it! Daran, what about dates? Men?"

"What about them?" Humor seemed to be one possible out.

"There should be men in your life."

"There are."

His challenge came quickly. "Like who?"

The impish lift of her dark brows belied her near-thirty years. "Like . . . you, my father, Hamilton Brody, Dr. Immlat, Tom Sellick. Even Jonathan deFalco!" She chuckled at the thought.

24

Glen Roberts found nothing amusing in her listing. With a note of exasperation, he began again, only to stop himself as quickly. "Daran . . . ach, it's really none of my business, is it?"

A soft laugh filtered through the young woman's pink-glossed lips. "No, it isn't, Glen. But I do appreciate your concern. And, believe me, I'm doing just fine." It was no lie, yet the devoted attorney had no way of knowing how much it would have been five years ago. She had never told him, or his bubbly wife, Lois, or any of the other friends and colleagues she'd come to know here in Connecticut. It was part of the past, and had no relevance here.

"Okay, hon. Listen, would you like me to be in on that meeting with Charles?" His words broke through her thoughts, bringing her sharply back to the present.

The faint shake of dark wavy hair was a unconscious gesture. "No, thanks." She declined his offer gracefully. "I think I'd better face the music myself, since it was my big mouth that brought him here to begin with. Whew, I still can't quite believe it."

The deep-intoned offer came one final time. "Well, if I can be of any help . . ."

Daran laughed, this time a light and airy sound as a new and particularly amusing thought came to her. "Where would I put you, Glen? This office can comfortably hold me and my desk. I'm pushing it for the senator. And if he happens to bring a typical entourage with him for effect, I may just have to move out myself!"

The resurgent trace of sarcasm was countered with gentle chiding. "Be generous, now, Daran. We're not all as efficient a one-person operation as you are! Say, what time would you like the Project meeting to be held on Tuesday night?"

"Seven-thirty? At your office?"

"Seven-thirty, it is. See you then."

"Bye-bye, Glen."

Heavy-fringed amber eyes slid to the face of her watch as Daran hung up the phone. Fifteen minutes till the senior tutorial. Rising quickly, she straightened the scattered mass of papers on her desk, opened her notebook, extracted a sheath of typed papers from the file cabinet and inserted it into the notebook. Then she clapped the whole thing soundly shut. A slim hand smoothed the pleats of her wool skirt, tucking the crepe blouse in more neatly. Turning for final inspection to the small mirror hanging on the back of the door, she grimaced. All her efforts to dress the part of the mature college professor were doomed to failure by the stubborn rebellion of the waves that framed her head and shoulders and the handful of freckles that last weekend's work in the garden had brought out. No suntan, only freckles. Such was her fate in life! With a low-muttered oath, she extracted a large tortoise-shell barrette from her pocketbook and secured the weight of hair from the sides back up into a semblance of a topknot at the crown of her head. A touch of mascara, a dab of blush, and a reapplication of lipstick—it would have to do.

Pausing only to adjust the thin strap of her high-heeled slingbacks more comfortably on her foot, she slung her pocketbook over her shoulder, hoisted her notebook and several reference books into her arms, draped her khaki trenchcoat over the lot, and left the office.

"I'm off for the tutorial, MaryAnne." Her soft voice carried to the ears of the blond-haired student/secretary busily at work at a desk in the large area beyond the separate offices. "If anyone wants me, I'll be back here by five, then I'll be leaving at about five-thirty for a dinner meeting at the hospital. Take any messages, okay?"

The young woman at the desk smiled easily. As opposed to some more ornery academicians, this professor was a peach to work for. Easy-going and compassionate, she inspired the trust of her students and, in the short semester and a half she had been at Trinity, had managed to extract from them superior quality work.

"Sure, Dr. Patterson. Oh, could you sign these letters before you leave? I'd like to have them in the mail this afternoon. And . . ." MaryAnne's voice lowered to a near-whisper as the professor reached for a pen and leaned awkwardly, laden as she was, to sign the letters on the desk. "I think that Jonathan deFalco is waiting to snare you somewhere along the hall out there." Her eyes brimmed with humor as she cocked her head toward the outer door of the office.

"Oh, dear." The last of the letters signed, Daran dropped the pen and sighed ruefully. "Is he making an absolute pest of himself?"

"Well, actually, it's not so bad. We've put him to work. You know, running errands and all. He's quite willing to do most anything as long as there is a chance he may catch sight of you."

The two shared a gentle laugh, then Daran shook her head regretfully. "I am sorry. He must be a nuisance. I'll see if I can talk him into—or out of—something," she offered feebly, wondering herself what the best method would be of curing a flagrant case of puppy love. All the formal training in the world—wasn't psychology supposed to be her field?—had not prepared her for the pure adoration that poor Jonathan deFalco held for her. The advances of men she had learned to parry quite successfully; boys were another matter. At age eighteen, Jonathan was idealistic, vulnerable, perhaps slightly homesick, and very much in love.

As young for his years as was Jonathan, the other student, MaryAnne, was mature. "Don't worry, Dr. Patterson. We'll handle it. You have enough to worry about."

This, coming from a young woman who carried a full course load, worked part-time to support herself, and had barely enough time to do anything for the pure fun of it, was a humbling experience.

"Thanks, MaryAnne." The words seemed inadequate, even accompanied as they were by a supportive hand on the younger woman's shoulder, as Daran headed for the hall. How fortunate she was to have met students of the caliber of this one!

The week flew by in typical hectic pace, allowing Daran a minimum of time to ponder her upcoming confrontation with Senator Andrew Charles. Though word of his impending visit weighed heavily in the news releases, there was no mention of the appointment at noon at Trinity. Daran kept it that way, fully convinced that the more private her discussion with the senator, the greater her chances of affecting his attitude on the bill. This was not the time for high visibility. As she reasoned, the political ego was a fragile thing. Her press statements may have already injured the senator's pride. This meeting would be her opportunity to assuage that pride, then gently move onward. It was feminine wiliness at its least sexual and most practical.

Friday night was spent reviewing her notes, committing to memory the latest facts on the status of children in the state, refreshing her mind of others which would be pertinent to their discussion. Saturday morning, after several early family counseling sessions at the hospital, Daran wound her way through the crosstown traffic to the Trinity campus, parking in her reserved space, then making a beeline for her office. It had been her best intention to freshen up there before the arrival of the visiting dignitary. Much as she would have preferred to return home to change in the interim, the thirty-minute drive from downtown to Simsbury precluded that possibility. As it was, she had carefully chosen her clothes this morning with a mind to presenting an image of competence and maturity. For the occasion she wore a brown-and-white tweed suit, replete with blazer, vest, and slim-cut skirt, a soft white silk blouse, a major concession to femininity, as were the high-heeled pumps that added an extra three inches to her five-foot-six height. Now she needed the extra height to boost her confidence.

For a brief moment as she struggled to fasten the cascade of brown waves into a semblance of a coil at the nape of her neck, she thought back on that confidence. It had been so strong, a very part of her from childhood, until that shattering few months she had spent with Bill. Mercifully that period of her life was over. No longer was she the starry-eyed romantic she had been then. Older and wiser now, she had finally grown up.

Three times she redid the knot, each time cursing her fingers for their clumsiness, her hair for its curliness, then, finally, herself, for her nervousness. What was wrong with her? Politics and politicians had been a part of her life until she had sworn off both five years ago. This, today, was merely a temporary dabbling which could not be avoided. Once her message was received, in person, by the senator, there would be no further need to mix. Glen would handle the Washington lobby while she held the home front. For no lure, regardless how potent, could get her to Washington. No lure, whatsoever!

A half-composed final exam sat idly on the desk before her, its blank pages mocking her attempt at concentration, while slowly the minute hand moved from the nine to the ten, then on to the eleven. It was at two minutes before noon that the sound of voices heralded the expected arrival. The building was largely deserted, only a smattering of professors and students occupying it on this early spring weekend afternoon. The secretarial staff had long since vanished, not to be seen or heard until Monday morning. It was an ideal time for a private business meeting with the senator, when interruptions would be nonexistent. Now, as the voices grew louder, Daran wondered fleetingly whether she should have had Glen here after all. But that was water over the dam; it was too late now.

"Dr. Patterson?" Jonathan deFalco's beaming face took her by surprise, until she heard his eager words. "These men were looking for your office. Since I was, ah, just hanging around, I thought I'd act as a guide."

In a flash she was on her feet and by the door, where she put as maternal an arm as possible around the shoulder of the boy, subtly rewarding him even as she turned him around to usher him out. It was at that point that her eye fell on the two men behind him.

"Dr. Patterson," the nearer of the two began, extending a friendly hand in her direction, "I'm John Hollings. We spoke on the phone. It's a pleasure to meet you." A nattily dressed man of medium height and fair complexion, he greeted her with sincerity and an unmistakable sparkle of appreciation in his brown eyes. This, however, was lost on her, as her attention was drawn inexorably to the man to his left and slightly behind. This last of the three was by far the tallest, the most compelling, and, up to this point, the most silent. "This is Senator Charles, Dr. Patterson." His aide proceeded to make the introduction, then stood aside to let the legislator by.

The aura of strength that surrounded the man served now to obliterate all else to either side of him. Slowly stepping forward, he offered her his hand. It took every ounce of poise she could muster for Daran to steady her own hand as it surrendered to the encompassment of his. Voice willed to evenness, eyes to directness, she spoke. "How do you do, Senator? This is an honor."

30

"The honor is mine." The voice was low and soft, its drawl as self-assured as everything else about the man. Steadfastly he held her hand long after all shaking motion had ceased. "May we talk in here?" he asked, his eyes releasing hers to look over her shoulder at the small office behind.

Only as she nodded did he release her hand. Instantly she thrust it into the pocket of her suit jacket, its tingling sensation barely diminished by contact with the soft lining. Then, looking up, she caught the knowing glint in his eye. It was enough to restore her senses. "Yes," she stated smoothly, "but it's not very large. Perhaps—" she glanced meaningfully at John Hollings "—we can use the conference room down the hall."

"No, this will be fine," the deep-intoned voice came back in command. Then, the sandy head turned to face his aide. "John, why don't you let Mr. deFalco guide you back to the parking lot. Dr. Patterson and I will meet you there in ten minutes."

With his facial expression totally hidden from her, Daran could only react to his words. Ten minutes—was that all she was to be granted? After the hours she had spent and would continue to spend on the Child Advocacy Project, this man, who had it in his power to so greatly affect the lives of the children for whom she fought, would give her ten minutes. *Ten minutes!* How typical! He was no different from the others. Bristling, she turned on her heel and strode into her office, pausing at its far side with her back to the door, hands crossed over her chest, until she heard the soft click of the closing door. Prepared to do battle, she whirled about—and her breath caught.

CHAPTER 2

He was magnificent. There was no other way to describe him. Not one of the magazine or newspaper pictures, or even the filmed TV spots, had done him justice. Outlined now against the stark white office door—the breadth of his shoulders totally covered the mirror which hung at eye level to her—he was a sight to behold. His dark navy suit was immaculately tailored and fit him to perfection, emphasizing the masculine form that tapered appealingly from shoulder to hip. His white shirt was a crisp foil for the suit, as well as the subtle paisley tie of maroon, navy, and gray. Highly polished oxfords glinted from beneath the cuffless trousers.

All this was taken in on the periphery of Daran's vision. For it was his face to which her attention was riveted. Evenly tanned, it was more angular than she had expected, the force of high cheekbones and a chiseled jaw bespeaking the inner strength for which he was renowned. His nose was straight, his lips firm and curving at the corners almost imperceptibly. Above it all, his eyes held her in their power, silver and warming with each passing second.

"I believe you were about to blast me, Dr. Patterson." Smooth as his casually lounging stance against the door, his voice was nearly her undoing. Frantically struggling to recall her objective, she blurted out the first thing that came to mind.

"Ten minutes doesn't give me much time, Senator Charles."

The gray eyes fell indolently to a wide-banded gold watch at his wrist. "Nine minutes and counting," he mocked softly.

It was his very mockery that steadied her. With a deep breath, she began. "My organization respects everything that you are trying to do in Washington." Even to her own ear, the wooden sound of her voice was awkward. "The Rights of Minors Act, if it passes, could be a noble first step. Your bill touches on all the major points—"

"Dr. Patterson," he interrupted, crossing his arms over his chest, "I didn't come here to listen to flattery, although —" again the faint mockery "—it is always appreciated. But let's get to the point, shall we? What are your objections?" His directness startled her, momentarily tying her tongue as she wondered exactly how blunt she dared be. "Well . . . ?" he prodded, glancing again at his watch for effect. Furious at his insolence, disgusted at her own timidity, she finally spoke.

"It's all watered down. The bill doesn't go far enough." There seemed no point in soft-pedaling her criticisms. "You've touched on all the critical matters of education, housing, health care, parental responsibility, legal representation, custody, adoption, and protection from abuse and neglect, but you simply don't go far enough." Pausing to catch her breath, she studied the intent face before her, but to no avail.

"Go on." His reaction, if any, was well hidden behind the mask of the politician. But, having been started on a subject so dear to her, Daran would have continued now even in the face of outright fury.

"Take the matter of health care. Whether it is some-

33

thing as urgent as the early treatment of cancer, or a thing as fundamental as good nutrition, or the simple right of a child to have his teeth straightened and save himself innumerable problems later in life—your general wording is not going to guarantee these things."

When she paused this time, it was for a totally different reason. For the placid mask had slipped to reveal an unexpected and, from her point of view, unappreciated, smugness. Deep inside, she wondered whether this overbearing man had heard a word she had just said. To her subsequent chagrin, the thought tumbled forth.

"You're looking particularly pleased with yourself, Senator. Am I missing something?" Her choice of wording could not have been worse, for the suggestive light which came to his eye.

"Oh, it's not *me* I'm pleased with. And, no, you're not missing a thing." With infinite slowness and devastating thoroughness, his eye traveled her length, his meaning crystal clear.

Indignance lifted her chin. "Did you hear what I've told you . . . about the Rights of Minors Act?"

"Uh-huh." His gaze locked once more with her own. This time the shiver that passed through her could not be suppressed. In its wake, her own mind began to recalculate.

Despite the image that had preceded him, she had planned to confront a senator, an esteemed higher-up of the United States governmental structure. Instead, she found herself face-to-face with a man and acutely aware of her own existence as a woman. Her challenge was an impulsive one. "Senator, may I ask a straight question?" At his immediate nod, she plundered on. "What did you expect to find when you arrived here today?" The male mind was often more simple to understand at its most base stage. In this assumption she was right on target.

Without hesitation of voice or lapse of eyehold, the senator confirmed her suspicion. "I pictured a Dr. Patterson who was very intelligent, very dedicated, and very plain. I was right on the first two counts."

Ignoring the lefthanded compliment, Daran bristled at the chauvinistic edge to his arrogance. "And why must a woman who is intelligent and dedicated be *plain,* if I might ask?" Her hands had moved to her hips and sat there now in subtle provocation. At that particular moment, she was unaware of exactly how far from plain she was. With the wisps of curls escaped from their tentative bonds and setting her face in a sensual frame, the flush of anger, excitement, or both on her cheeks, and the sparks of gold flickering in her eyes, she was a stunning woman.

"Obviously, she is not." For the first time his broad smile graced her with a view of those even white teeth that supposedly won hearts over right and left. But Daran's heart had been won and broken long ago, in another state, by another man. It would take more than a bright smile to win her over this time.

As she steeled herself for an appropriate response, her adversary moved fluidly from the door and slowly approached her. "You get more beautiful as you get worked up. That takes skill." He mocked her and she detested it, yet words eluded her. Mesmerized by the eyes that surveyed her face before settling, finally, on her lips, she felt the beginnings of a quiver of something strange within her, then the moment abruptly snapped.

"Come on. Time's up." A large tan hand took her elbow.

"But I haven't had a chance to say anything!" she protested, eyes rounding in dismay that the audience was over so soon with nothing to prove for the effort.

"Oh, you began quite well," he assured her, drawing her beside him toward the door. Suddenly he halted as sharp

35

eyes scanned the room. Frowning, he asked absently, "Do you have a purse or something that you cannot do without for an hour or so?"

Bewildered, she merely stared. "Where am I going?"

Nonchalance ruled his every move as he spotted, then reached for, her pocketbook, not for a minute releasing her arm. "I'm hungry. We're going out for lunch."

"But I don't understand—" The door slammed shut behind them as he set a steady pace toward the hall.

From what seemed to be a full head above her, he looked down indulgently. "Lunch. You know, that meal in the middle of the day which one normally consumes to revive oneself?"

"I know what lunch is—" embarrassment painted a faint rose on her cheek "—but I thought you had only ten minutes to spare. What about that busy schedule you legislators supposedly have? What about that image of the man-about-town grabbing a sandwich on the run?"

They reached the hall, then the stairs. Daran was all too well aware of the hand that tightened beneath her elbow to compensate for the precariousness of her high-heeled step as they spiraled down the two flights.

"I need nourishment if I'm going to keep to that schedule. And a sandwich on the run only risks crumbs on my suit. We have an hour." He went on without a breath. "Where do you suggest we go?" But before she could open her mouth to venture a possibility, Drew Charles answered his own question. "How about—" he cast a glance her way "—oh, I forget that you're new here. There's a terrific little place you'll never have heard of—"

"Athena's?" A tight grin of her own escaped as they approached the exit.

Silver eyes reflected his surprise graciously. "You've heard of it?"

"Even we professional women have to eat," she retorted

36

pertly. "And it does happen to have the best Greek salad around."

"Salad? My God, no wonder you're so slim. I could go for some baked lamb right about now. Hey, John!" They had arrived, slightly breathlessly on Daran's part, in the parking lot and the waiting aide came running. "Listen, John. Dr. Patterson and I have some unfinished business to attend to. Why don't you go ahead to the insurance seminar. Tell them I'm on my way. Stan and Dewey should be there already. Give me an hour."

With a mischievous wink in Daran's direction, John grinned widely at his boss. "Sure thing. Say—" he lowered his voice to a tone of mock secrecy "—do you need any money?" The senator's game plan was no mystery to his friend. In the instant Daran sensed that she was but one and the latest of many women to be given the rush. Before she could demur, she found herself drawn in the opposite direction from the aide as the tall man beside her called over his shoulder, "No, thanks. The lady is loaded."

"What?" Protest finally exploded.

"Point out your car and let me have the keys." Reversing the line of thought left Daran perplexed. Mutely she regarded the commanding figure as though he were from another planet. "The keys?" he repeated, looking down on her as though *she* had temporarily lost her senses, which she had, she concluded silently, as her docile hand began a search of her bag for the large and heavy key ring.

"Your car," the deep voice at her ear prodded. "Which one is it?" Simultaneously he spotted the very visible RE-SERVED FOR DR. PATTERSON sign and, within a minute, had removed the keys from her hand, unlocked the door, and gallantly seated her on the passenger side before appearing behind the wheel.

Suddenly the scene took on slapstick proportions, drawing a spontaneous fit of laughter from the hitherto sober

37

Dr. Patterson. With the slam of the door beside him and a low oath as he groped beneath the seat for the lever to give himself more leg room, the distinguished senator from Connecticut turned to his passenger, sighing with relief as the seat finally slid back. "Now what in the devil is so funny?"

Barely suppressing further mirth, she angled sideways in her seat, back flush against the door. "This whole thing is absurd," she began, tapered fingers splayed across her chest as she steadied her breathing. "I was prepared for a very formal discussion with a supposedly dignified legislator, and what do I get? I get spirited away like a thief in the night, in my own car, at my own expense, and—" She broke off as laughter erupted once more. "And you look so funny, crammed into this car like . . . like . . ."

"Go on," the deep voice dared her. When she could not, he did so for her. "Like a clown at the circus." As he scowled good-naturedly, she laughed again, pausing only so as not to miss a word of his rebuttal. "Let me tell you, lady, it's a crime against those lovely long legs of yours to squish them up so close to the wheel. And although I like small cars myself, this Beetle is ridiculous. No wonder they stopped manufacturing them years ago. And—" he went on strongly, quite adept at speaking off the cuff, as his job must demand "—you may think it hilarious to be rushed around, dodging here and there, but if you had a face as easily recognized as this one, you'd do the same."

The boyish intensity of his complaint, intoned in such a low and very masculine timber, struck a sympathetic cord in Daran. Yet she could not resist one further dig. "I would have thought that you'd want every last bit of publicity; or is that only during an election year?" Wasn't it the image? Wasn't that how it had been with Bill? Her sober undertone instantly spread to the senator.

"This may come as a surprise to you, Dr. Patterson, but

38

there is indeed a very private man somewhere deep down inside this outwardly public shell. And that very private man needs to let it all out, as they say, every once in a while. Without the press. Without his staff. Without a ubiquitous public looking over his shoulder."

The atmosphere in the car suddenly grew heavy with the turn of the conversation. Guilt-ridden at having been as insensitive as she must have appeared, Daran stared for long moments at the steel-hard silver-edged gaze that speared her.

"I'm sorry," she whispered. "I meant no harm." The softness of her voice rang with sincerity; her own eyes echoed the apology. Feeling herself about to wither beneath his penetrating stare, she turned to look out the window. The fingers on her chin took her by surprise when they effortlessly tilted her face back to his.

Even before his eyes dropped to her lips, she felt the pull. It was an intangible force, rippling from man to woman and back, an invisible current, until the two pairs of lips were no more than a breath apart. With one hand on the back of the seat and another on the dashboard, he did not touch her, until gently, lightly, his lips whispered over the corners of her mouth, enticing a response by virtue of their very innocence. Aware only vaguely of what was happening, Daran fought to resist this powerful magnetism. But the mind was suddenly a thing apart from the body. With a helpless sigh her lips parted, to be met an instant later by the full force of a kiss which, in its soulful tenderness, robbed her of breath. When it ended and the awesome bond was finally broken, she recoiled belatedly, blotting the back of her hand against lips which continued to burn for long moments.

"I'm sorry." Even with the two words spoken, the consummate politician was back to form. "I had no right to

39

do that," he went on, calmly, level-headed, obviously un-moved. "I know very little about you."

In truth, it was her anger at his total composure that spawned. Daran's instant indignation. "You're right. You do know very little about me. And you shouldn't have done that." As soon as the words were out, shame washed over her. She had invited his kiss; she had been every bit at fault as he. And she had enjoyed it. Damn it, she had! Perhaps that was what bothered her the most. For five years she had been immune to that type of physical re-sponse. For five years the very thought of a kiss such as that would have repulsed her. Was this some kind of fluke? Or was she once again vulnerable?

As though sensing the inner torment he had caused, Drew Charles deftly started the car. "Come on, let's get something to eat. We've got only fifty minutes left." The smile in his voice came through in his words and spread contagiously to her lips. With a shy glance his way, she nodded in acquiescence, then settled back in the car for the brief but silent ride to the restaurant.

Once again the absurdity of the situation nearly brought a disbelieving laugh to the surface. To be sitting in her worn-out VW with a United States senator at the wheel, in total silence, no less—it was remarkable.

"Yes, I do enjoy the silence," he read her thoughts too easily for comfort, then drew the car easily alongside the curb in front of the small, secluded restaurant. It was as though those few moments of quiet in the car had served to ease the transition from spirited male to stately politi-cian. For, once out of the car and inside the restaurant, the senator was every bit the senator, greeting friendly faced patrons and his personal friends, the owners of the inti-mate establishment, with a typically broad smile. Throughout their arrival, he was even-toned, suave, dig-nified, and impeccably behaved. Had it not been for a recurring vivid reminder at the quick of her pulse, Daran might have imagined that other, more impulsive side entirely. Not knowing quite what to expect now, she let him take the conversational lead when finally they had been shown to a quiet booth at the rear of the place and were seated. Drew ordered for them both; with unrivaled speed, his lamb and her Greek salad were before them. There were definite advantages to being a somebody, she mused silently as she tried to calculate exactly how much time remained of their allotted hour.

"Tell me about yourself, Dr.—it's Daran, isn't it?"

While she would have preferred a less personal and more relevant topic of discussion, she was in no mood to fight. "Yes." The formal appellation did seem strange. Much as she had earned the title, she had never quite been able to see herself as a doctor, albeit of philosophy.

"How did you get such an unusual name?" For a lean man, he ate quickly and heartily. Now, as he sat back to watch her pick at her salad, she wondered whether he had skipped breakfast or whether he had simply been too busy showering smiles on an adoring gathering to indulge in the fare offered.

With a deep breath to rid herself of this persistent cynicism, she explained. "My mother wanted Karen, my father Donna. Somehow Daran was the end result." It was a frequently asked question, one whose answer invariably led to others, as was the case now.

"Did your parents settle every difference as satisfactorily?" The strange phrasing, or perhaps it was the very subtle edge to his words, made an impression on her. But that analysis was for another time. For now he had asked a question and deserved an answer.

"I don't really know. My father died in an accident when I was a small child. I don't remember him very clearly."

Sharp silver eyes studied her closely. "Does it bother you to talk about it?"

Blushing under his scrutiny, she shrugged. "No. But there's not much to say. My mother remarried soon after and my father became a very vague memory."

"You're from Cleveland, aren't you?"

A dark eyebrow arched. "So you did check up on me."

There was mischief on his face when he grinned, as well as a touch of guilt that she felt, against her will, was endearing. "It's part of my job. I have to know the kind of people with whom I'm dealing. You appear to have led a relatively stable life—no great traumas, nothing approaching the scandalous, everything coming up roses." The gist of the conversation made her choke on her lettuce. A small cough and a sip of water later, she struggled to still the shaking of her knees. Obviously his researchers had not dug deep enough, though, Lord knows, everything had been done at the time to ensure silence. Did she have Bill to thank for that? she wondered spitefully. To her chagrin, her face reflected these innermost thoughts.

"Are you all right?" he asked, strangely concerned. "You look as though you pricked yourself on one of those roses."

"Very perceptive," she mumbled beneath her breath, suddenly all appetite having vanished. "But we didn't come here to discuss roses, did we?" It would be much safer to discuss the Child Advocacy Project, she reasoned, as she put down her fork and sat back in her seat, feigning a relaxation she was far from feeling.

"Do you enjoy living in Connecticut?" Strong, bronze fingers twirled the stem of an empty wineglass, as his own state of relaxation appeared to be maddeningly genuine.

"Yes. It's a beautiful state."

"What brought you here from San Francisco?"

Jolted again by the span of his knowledge of her, Daran

sensed that he was testing her. Poise under fire was the key, if such was the case. Assuming that he was ignorant of her time with Bill, he could do absolutely nothing to intimidate her.

"A job."

"Did you need the work?"

"Now," she chided in a voice laden with mock sternness, "weren't you the one who said I was loaded?"

He cleared his throat in amusement. "That was before I saw your car. It's quite a collector's item."

"It runs." He could mock most anything but her car; it had seen her through many things and it got her where she wanted to go.

"But you didn't need the money, since you live in Simsbury. Your address has a fine ring about it."

Suddenly defensive, she explained. "It belonged to a friend of the family. When I decided to move east, I was given the use of the place. I'm actually renting it."

With a slight shake of his sandy head and a short wave of his hand, the senator dismissed her explanation. "That's not my business. But I would like to know why you work as hard as you do. I'm told that you have irrepressible energy. Actually—" he grinned "—you'd make an excellent politician's wife, if that is the case."

"*Never!*" The force of her denial took the senator completely off guard, wiping the grin from his lips. Then, as quickly as the explosion fused, it fizzled. Biting her lip, her composure was negligible. Mercifully the waiter brought coffee at that moment, giving her the extra time to recover. Why the discussion had centered on herself, she could not fathom; but she vowed to remedy the situation.

"How about you, Senator. Have you been a lifelong resident of Connecticut? You'll have to excuse me," she tacked on another thought, "but I don't have the staff for research that you do, and since I haven't been here that

43

long, I haven't followed your family history." Praying that her words did not hold the hint of disdain that shadowed her thoughts, she awaited his response.

For a moment it appeared that he would refuse to answer. His eye held a lazy glint, his mouth a harder line. He studied her for something, yet she could not, for the life of her, know what. Eventually he straightened, added milk and sugar to his coffee with a hand whose blond hairs sparkled, then eyed her with full sincerity. There was neither mockery nor humor. As she had been warned, the eye contact was direct; she would believe anything he told her.

"My family goes back several generations in this state. Politics seems to be inbred. My grandfather was in the House of Representatives, my father in the Governor's chair. The Senate is a first for the family." As he spoke, inner concentration seemed to take him from her to some distant place.

Her own words surprised her. "You must feel proud of your own accomplishments."

Slowly he returned to the present. "There is always something else to do. It may seem a very glamorous job to the outsider, but I've never worked as hard in my life. But, yes, there is that inner reward when something you work for becomes law."

"Are your parents here in the state?" For some reason she found herself curious about the man. Perhaps it was the psychologist in her; perhaps it was the memory of that kiss that the man within the senator had bestowed. Regardless, the question popped out.

Drew's voice grew softer. "My father still lives here. My mother died many years ago. Politics did not agree with her." It was a simple statement, but one which carried a wealth of meaning. Daran was frankly surprised that he had made it to her, a relative stranger. It was as though,

44

in the intimacy of this small restaurant, all would be sealed within when lunch was over. This was an isolated interlude, a change of pace for them both. As she looked now at the face across the narrow table, the wear and tear of ten years of public life was clearly visible. There were laugh lines aplenty radiating from the corners of his eyes, shadows of the ever-present smile around his mouth. And the forehead which nobly bore that boyish swath of sandy-brown hair also bore its share of worry lines. For a fleeting moment she felt unexpected sympathy for him—until she caught herself and staggered back to reality. No one had drafted him; he had enlisted, then fought hard to land the job. There were more than enough side benefits of his position to compensate for the headaches it entailed. The truly sad thing was what it could do to others in its wake.

"Your reputation is a fine one, from what I hear. Several of my neighbors have raved about the work you did in the House on that hazardous waste-disposal bill. How many terms were you a representative?" Her return to a more formal discussion succeeded in recharging the conversation as it sidestepped a potentially delicate matter.

His eyes acknowledged her tactic; his smile approved of it. "I served three terms—six years in all."

"What made you decide to run for the Senate?" Unconsciously she licked her dry lower lip. His gaze flickered toward her tongue for a split second before returning to her amber eyes.

"The Senate is the upper house," he shrugged. "It seemed the natural thing to do."

"I don't believe that for a minute," she accused softly, impulsively. "Your reputation is based on your sense of conviction, not any tendency to go along for the ride." Realizing her impertinence, she lowered her eyes apologetically.

Perked up by her challenge, he sat forward, his voice

gentle. "Please don't hesitate to say what's on your mind. This is perhaps the most candid discussion I've had along these lines in . . . too long. And as for your sentiment, you are right." Conviction, that very thing she had dangled before him, placed an indelible mark on his words. "I ran for the Senate because I felt that there were broader matters, matters relating to laws which affected the entire country, to which I could make a viable contribution. The responsibility was greater; rather than being one of six representatives, I would be one of two senators. Rather than being up for reelection every two years, I could spend more time *doing* and less time campaigning." He looked sharply off to the side, again in a daydream. "I've long been in favor of a six-year, single-term presidency for that very reason. A man has to be free of that ever-present tug-of-war between conscience and constituent if he is to accomplish anything."

Daran had gotten more than she'd bargained for, and she was fascinated. The unbridled intrigue suffused in her expression must have struck a humorous chord in Drew, for, as quickly as he had grown serious, once again he slipped into easy banter.

"You're not taking notes on this, are you?" A tawny brow lifted to offset the twist of his lips in amusement. "Is there a reporter lurking beneath that lovely cascade of chocolate curls, or an incipient psychoanalytical genius waiting in the wings to study the loathsome legislative mind?" There was a note of truth in his teasing; he must have sensed her disdain for the political breed. With every attempt to cover her lapse, she laughed aloud, shaking those same curls of which he had spoken.

"No, I'm just me, the intelligent, dedicated, and sometimes nosy child psychologist." Actually, at that point, Daran began to wonder exactly which me was sitting so comfortably and complacently over this leisurely lunch,

46

when so many critical issues were running out of time. What had happened to her cause? As a spokeswoman, she had bottomed out. Where was the sharp tongue that had brought the senator here in the first place?

The long arm across from her flexed as the gold watch made a menacing appearance. Again her thoughts were on the table. "It looks like we've got to be running. John won't be able to hold those men off for too much longer." As he spoke, he motioned to the owner with his hand, extracted a sum of money from his pocket—to her surprise—and paid the bill in full, leaving a generous tip for the waiter before escorting Daran back to her car. Once inside, he headed for the headquarters where the insurance seminar was to be held.

"I thought you didn't have any money on you." She cast a sidelong glance at the features, rugged now in profile as he drove.

"It's a standard joke between John and me. There are those legislators who never carry a dime. For some reason they have the gall to expect others to pick up the tab. But then, one finds strange personalities in Washington, D.C., let me tell you."

In a moment of flashback, her "I can imagine" was an understatement. Bill was the strangest, most unpredictable, most irresponsible, most despicable . . . the list went on and on. But to what point? It was over and done. Washington could have him!

All too soon, though she couldn't understand why, the car pulled up before a large granite structure that dominated the western fringe of downtown Hartford.

"Well, Daran." He turned in his seat, with the little leeway the small foreign car allowed, and faced her. "Thank you for a very enjoyable meeting."

"Meeting?" she coughed out incredulously, overrun with guilt at how unlike a meeting it had been. What was she ever going to say to the advisory board of the Project when it met next week? "We didn't get much of a chance to discuss your bill, or my project, for that matter."

"It was still a very productive meeting."

"Is that what you people call it—very productive?"

"Now, now," he scolded with a teasing half-smile. "That cynicism is showing again. The least you could do is to go into this with an open mind."

Amber eyes widened in bemusement. "Into what?"

But her query went unheeded. With a glance over her shoulder and out the window, Drew climbed fluidly from the car and guided her around to the driver's side. Then, leaning down to talk for a moment longer, he was all business, the smooth-talking senator from Connecticut. "We'll discuss it more another time." He shot a second glance toward the building, then went quickly on. "Do me a favor? Between now and then, write out everything you think is wrong with the bill. List the pluses too. I want everything in fine detail. I'll get back to you within the next week." The orders flew fast from the tongue of this imperial commander. Knowingly he stemmed her imminent protest with an unexpected and seemingly irrelevant question. "When is commencement this year?"

Frowning in puzzlement, she searched her jumbled mind for the date. "The twenty-third of May, I think."

"Good. Plan to be in Washington the following week."

"But I can't go to Washington!"

"The first trip will be an introductory one. I want you to meet the staff," he continued, ignoring her outcry. "Then we can plot the rest of the summer."

"I won't go to Washington!" The slight change in her choice of words was an honest one. Yes, she *could* certainly go to Washington if she wished. With the semester over, the time would be open. But she did not wish it, therefore she *would* not go.

The gray eyes that bore into her carried a deliberate challenge as he leaned closer and lowered his voice to a more intimate drawl. "You'll be there." Then he rounded the front of the car and bounded up the steps of the building.

"I'm not going to Washington!" she yelled, leaning across the seat to the open window on the curb side. But the broad back receded and the senatorial ears never heard. At the top of the steps three other men waited to envelop this central figure and usher him into the building to face the roomful of eager constituents, his public.

Softly she repeated once more, "I'm not going to Washington." Oddly it seemed more a prayer than a declaration, and a feeble one at that. Determined to dismiss the preposterous suggestion as just that, she put the key in the ignition, then reached a foot for the gas pedal. Sliding nearly out of the seat for lack of leg to reach the distant pedal, she muttered a silent oath, then slid the seat forward once more. *The arrogance of the man,* she fumed, *to take over my car as though he owned it!* Diverted in this way by a petty issue, the matter of a trip to Washington was temporarily shelved. In fact the entire visit with the honorable Senator Andrew Charles fell victim to the usual slew of Saturday afternoon errands, such that his name did not cross her mind until later that afternoon when Glen Roberts called.

"How did it go, hon?" he asked enthusiastically.

"Not bad, Glen. But we didn't really have much time to get to all the major points. He asked me to compile a written summary of our criticisms for him to see."

"When?"

Good old direct Glen! "Ah, he was pretty vague about that," she hedged. "He said he would try to get back to me within a week or so."

"Terrific! Did he sound interested in our work?"

Again she fudged the specifics. "He seemed . . . open-minded, if that's what you mean." Recalling his use of that very term in conversation with her, Daran squirmed uncomfortably.

"And you are tired and don't really feel like going into detail about it, right?"

She smiled. "Right."

"Okay, hon. Another time. We're on our way out anyway. Any plans for tonight?" he asked, as if he didn't know the answer. The whole world loved Saturday night —except Daran Patterson.

"As a matter of fact, yes. I have an exciting date with a quiche Lorraine. It's going to hopefully put me in the mood to write that article for the *AmPsych Bulletin*. It could be a very productive evening." Again she cringed at the echo of another's words. Productive—that seemed to be the word of the day.

"I hope so, Daran. Talk with you first of the week."

With the phone cradled on its receiver, Daran sauntered idly into the living room and slouched carelessly into a large upholstered chair. Slowly she looked around at her lavish surroundings. For herself, her own tastes ran along much more simple lines than the plush carpeting and thick-cushioned sofas all in stark white and accented with pillows of rich brown and gold, and scattered brass-rimmed end tables. The fireplace was large and open and utterly unsuited for a fire, planted as it was with a vast assortment of shade-loving plants and ferns. Abstract paintings and lithographs stared down from the walls—all the property of the owner of the house. In fact, the only rooms which bore the stamp of the current resident were her bedroom and the study, both crammed with personal material in gross contrast to the seemingly neutral splendor of the living room, kitchen, and the master bedroom, which she had shunned.

Tucked away on this quiet hillside in Simsbury, the house was a lovely getaway for Daran. Friendly faces abounded at the local shopping center, yet she was left alone on this, her hillside. Even the few neighbors whose houses were reputed to exist in each its own burrow around the rise had been invisible in the six months she had lived here. She had her house; she had a small garden plot in the back; she had the cover of a thick-grown forest to shield her from the world—what more could she ask?

Yet, for the first time in many months, loneliness was a tangible thing. Why, on this particular night, had it returned to haunt her? Had the thought of Washington, of Bill earlier in the day, stimulated her sensitivities? Had things been different, had Bill been a different type of person, had his ambition been private rather than geared toward the public sector, Washington might have been her home now. But it was not, and never would be, her home —not if *she* had any say in the matter!

Bristling with determination, she changed into jeans and a T-shirt, then put a pre-baked quiche in the oven to heat. Gently torn lettuce lined a small wooden bowl, topped with several tomato wedges and handful of cucumber slices, by the time the quiche was warm. Yet the sight of the finished salad brought thoughts of that one she had eaten at lunch, and Daran was able only to pick and push with disinterest.

Disconcerted, she quickly cleaned the kitchen, then retreated to her study to work. It was hopeless; concentration eluded her even here in her very private bastion. Pen in hand, she stared at the blank sheet of paper on the desk. Cap of pen in mouth, she let her eye roam the room aimlessly. Tip of pen tapping paper, her patience wore thin, until, finally, with a soft curse, she dropped the writing tool entirely and gave up.

Similar fates met the television, then the radio in turn.

51

Nothing seemed to please her. Restlessly she stalked from room to room, a caged animal awaiting its release. But from what? She was a free and independent woman, answering to no one. What, then, could explain the coil of tension that was wound up within her? Why, so suddenly, had it appeared?

The black of night beckoned from room to room beyond each windowpane. It was out there—the emptiness—reflected in the image of herself upon the glass. She stared. Slowly she turned to pace to another spot. Nowhere could she find a remedy for the dull ache that gnawed at her.

Returning to the living room, her eye fell on the large key ring that lay on the coffee table by her purse. He had known just which key to use, precisely how to spark her tired old VW to life, even which roads would take him to his destination with a minimum of traffic. He was obviously a man who believed in efficiency, a man—from his record—who got things done. Why, then, had he wasted a good hour and a half, all told, with her today? What was his motive? As sure as she had to acknowledge him as the best-looking man she had seen in a long time, she knew that he would have a very definite motive for every single thing he did.

A frivolous moment's digression brought recollection of his kiss, so short and sweet and strong. In memory, her lips burned anew at their contact with his. In memory, she recalled her near mindlessness at that instant. Then, in a far greater span of memory, the parade of men dodging in and out of her life during the past five years flashed before her. Many had tried; none had succeeded. After Bill she wanted no part of the male ego, the male libido. The male intellect was a different matter. That she could respect. Over the years some of her most rewarding intellectual relationships had been with men, with colleagues of hers at the college, the hospital, even in the Project.

Today she had been impressed with his intellect. No doubt he was as bright as they said. And companionable. That had surprised her even as it puzzled her. But the other she did not need. That kiss had been a mistake from the word go. If only she had pulled back or turned her head or fended him off with her hands; hadn't she become expert at doing just that? Then why hadn't she this time? And why did the memory of him disquiet her so?

In the idle mind, frustration mushroomed into anger. This was not just any man who had overturned her peace of mind. This was a United States senator, an active member of the political establishment. He was no different from the others, with his cocksureness and his arrogance. And she, supposedly more experienced and wise to the ways of such men, had fallen for his kiss as many another must have done. Oh, yes, he wanted something. Subservience was the name of his game. The senator issues the orders, as he had done in those last few minutes, and assumes that the world is eager to please his every whim. It was appalling. And she wanted no part of it. Senator Andrew Charles could just take his Rights of Minors Act and blow it—if bedroom antics were the prerequisite to compromise.

The gentle chime of the doorbell contrasted sharply with her mood, mellowing it but faintly, as she rose from her seat. Was it Glen and Lois, checking up on her again, after their own big night out? Several times before, they had driven up, stopping in to say hello—to drag her from her books, no doubt—if the lights were on, passing on quietly home if all was dark. Stupidly she had left the lights burning brightly, a sure sign of invitation. And it was only ten o'clock; how could she feign exhaustion, even though the last thing she felt up to was a cheery visit?

A sigh of resignation blended with the repeat of the door chimes as she grabbed the knob and pulled the door

53

open. Daran had been grossly mistaken. Before her stood neither Glen nor Lois, nor any of the others who fell under the category of friends who might drop in at ten o'clock on Saturday night. Before her stood the one she least expected, the one whose presence had lingered, against her will, in her mind for much of the evening, the one who had touched off the very fit of temper that had seized her moments earlier. Before her, tie loosened, jacket slung over a finger draped on his shoulder, arm resting indolently against her door jamb, was Senator Andrew Charles.

"I believe we have some unfinished business to attend to." He spoke softly. "May I come in?"

Never in the weeks to come would Daran understand what possessed her, at that moment, to do what she did. Questions raced rampant about her mind. Emotions seesawed precariously round and about them. Better judgment struggled for its hearing, but to no avail. For, above the silence of her intellect, some other force bid her stand back and let the fellow in. Which she did. Promptly. Quietly. Graciously. It was, indeed, her own hand that closed the door on the dark of night as the senator entered her home.

CHAPTER 3

"Very nice," he murmured, his eye perusing the chic decor as he moved confidently to the center of the living room. Her own appraisal was no less sharp, encompassing the fine fabric of his formal tux, its satin-striped pant legs emphasizing his length, the starched white shirt, now opened at the neck to exaggerate his even tan, stressing the broad expanse of shoulder beneath. But neither the elegance of his dress nor the sureness of his step could hide the obvious.

"You look tired." Her quiet evaluation brought a wry smile to his lips.

"Believe it or not, this is my fourth stop this evening. There was a cocktail party at the home of the chairman of the state committee—" his fingers were counting them off, one by one, "—then a reception at the aircraft executives' club, then a dinner—a small one for forty people," he mocked, "at the home of one of my supporters in West Hartford. You don't happen to have a cup of coffee, do you?"

Incredulity held Daran immobile. Eyes widened, she could only stare at this unexpected visitor. His own nonchalance, in contrast, was remarkable and perplexing. "How did you find your way up here?" She finally managed to get out a feeble question. "Do you carry your files around with you, or do you simply memorize the addresses of your constituents? Or—" she cocked her head with faint amusement "—is your man Hollings out in the car?"

Silver eyes drilled her, just punishment for her sarcasm. "As I mentioned this afternoon, your address has a nice ring to it. It's an easy one to remember, if one knows the area as I do." Suppressing his own humor, he continued. "No, John is with his wife tonight. They had tickets to a concert at the Bushnell."

Unknowingly Daran arched an eyebrow in surprise. Though she had only met the man this morning and had seen him but in passing, she had quite naturally assumed John Hollings to be single. What was the role of a wife to be when her husband was sidekick to this inveterate bachelor? In the instant, a surge of sympathy for the woman engulfed her along with a germ of desire to talk one day with this poor soul. Perhaps she knew something that Daran did not!

"That coffee?" The man had approached and now stood an arm's length from her. Momentarily the faint scent of lingering after-shave mixed with the sweetness of brandy to tantalize her senses. Then that very nearness drove her away and toward the kitchen.

Muffled by the thick pile of the carpet in the hallway, his footsteps would have been unnecessary proof of his presence. For the prickling heat on the back of her neck, well beneath the heavy fall of waves that tumbled to her shoulders, announced his arrival in the kitchen seconds after her own. Determinedly she proceeded to set the coffee on to perk. Dismayed by his silent observation, she grew more self-conscious by the minute.

A surreptitious glance upward through the shade of her thick brown lashes revealed the rangy form leaning rest-fully against the counter. Unencumbered by the jacket, which lay draped across a chair in the living room, his

56

hands had taken refuge in the pockets of his trousers, drawing the black material taut over his muscled form. Embarrassed, she quickly averted her eyes.

Yet the fact remained that her T-shirt stretched over her breasts with more of a pull than she might have wished, that the fit of her faded denim jeans left room for nothing as heavy as wool tights, that her bare feet put nearly a foot of height between them. Here was a very tall man, even lounging as he was against the Formica of her kitchen counter.

Suddenly the reminder that this was *her* home and *her* kitchen brought her up a little straighter. Marveling at the casualness with which this master of presumption walked in and took over both at noontime and now this evening, she steeled herself for a confrontation. This was, after all, *her* Saturday night!

"It's the strangest thing," he began with velvet smoothness, as if anticipating her potential for resistance. His eye scanned her face, narrowing in thought.

"What is?"

"Your face. Your expressions. There must be some war going on in that head of yours. I noticed it this afternoon, and again now. You fluctuate from placidity to anger in an instant. Why?"

Annoyed at his perception, she shrugged. "We all have moods. Mine are no different from anyone else's. Perhaps I'm just not as good at camouflaging them. Or, perhaps—" she lifted her chin in defiance "—your position tends to intimidate people such that they pussyfoot around you."

Had she intended an insult, she failed miserably. The sadness in his smile gave credence to her accusation. "You may be right. Why aren't *you* intimidated? You aren't, you know. From the moment I met you today, you've been itching for a fight."

57

He was right—and that angered her even more. Yet, deep within one distant part of her, a fight was the last thing she wanted at the moment. Turning to lower the fire beneath the coffeepot, she busied herself gathering mugs, milk, and sugar, totally ignoring his contention. For the time being, her withdrawal was accepted. Silence reigned as she filled the mugs with coffee, then carried them to the kitchen table, a handsome piece of butcher block. It was surrounded by chrome-armed chairs. As she took a seat on one side, Drew eased himself down on the other, his gray eyes following her steadily, relentlessly.

Steam from the fresh brew, rising then dissipating into the air, seemed to be the only sign of life in the room. Daran's eyes held stubbornly to her fingers rimming her mug, studying them as though they were something strange and new to her. It was an awkward situation, to say the least. For, just when Daran gathered the courage to confront Drew as to his intentions, he deftly stole the wind from her sails with a word or two, spoken softly and often on an entirely different matter, thereby diverting her long enough for her fuse to spend itself harmlessly. A pro at handling people, he was a born diplomat.

For those first minutes the silence seemed cacophonous. Slowly and with feigned calmness, she sipped her coffee. Slowly and with genuine composure, he did the same. Daran's anger grew greater with every second that he failed to take the first step. Then, once again, as it had that afternoon in the car, the absurdity of the situation closed in on her. Laughing in spite of herself, she raised her eyes to those of the senator.

"You aren't at all what I expected," she offered softly.

"Is that good or bad?"

A shrug shook her slim shoulders as a shaft of distress passed across the erstwhile smoothness of her forehead. "I'm not sure."

58

He smiled. "There it goes again—the war." Then he executed another diversionary tactic. "This serenity is no less than a luxury. Do you come across it by design or by chance?"

Daran was quick to pick up on his implication. "If you are asking whether I choose to be alone on Saturday night, the answer is yes. I was actually planning to do some work."

His sandy head bent toward his watch. "It's pretty late. Did you get done what you wanted?"

"No."

"Why not?"

"I have no idea," she blurted back coolly, though indeed she did. It was the presence of strange and unbidden thoughts in her mind that blocked her usual creative mood, and this man was in no small way responsible.

"You mean," he challenged, "you have not yet made those lists I asked you to compile?"

It was only when she turned on him in dismay that the twinkle in his eye caught hers. He was goading her, baiting her. Should she fight? Even as she pondered the first blow, the voice that was her own came to her with unexpected evenness. "For a minute there, I thought you were serious."

"But I am. If you're going to spend the summer as a member of my staff, you've got to be prepared to produce."

Suddenly her temper triumphed. "I have no intention of spending the summer on your staff. My Lord, do you ever make wild assumptions! I have other plans—"

"Such as . . . ?"

"Such as lobbying for the Child Advocacy Project. Such as continuing to see my private patients at the hospital. Such as writing all of the journal articles that should have been done on any number of Saturday nights, but were

59

thwarted for one reason or the other." Furious now, her eyes were bright, her features animated. Here was one person whom Senator Charles did not have in his pocket! Yet her words to that effect died on her lips, halted abruptly by the inexplicably admiring glance which the man subsequently bestowed upon her.

"That's great!" He grinned, shaking his head in wonder. Intuitively Daran knew that he was not referring to her summer plans. His next words elaborated on that point. "You look terrific, all fired up like that! And I like your outfit, by the way. With your hair down, I mean." He reminded her of the wayward curls that had fallen from their coil that afternoon. *"Really* down. You look barely twenty-one." His grin, stretching with brilliant whiteness from ear to ear, jolted her far more than his words. Abruptly she stood and stormed from the kitchen toward the living room, clenching her fists in a bid for self-control. This was not going at all as she had expected, she mused, then caught herself up short. She had expected nothing! It had all been his doing. And exactly what did he expect— in addition to her traipsing down to Washington for the summer?

As if conjured up by her question, his tall form moved across the reflective surface of the window she faced. Beneath her intent eye he lowered himself into a corner of the sofa, stretched his legs out before him, crossing them nonchalantly at the ankles. Then he laid his head back on the cushion. For a breathstopping moment she wondered if he was asleep. They had a knack, these politicians, for catching a few winks here and there, so she had read, so she had seen in Bill. His particular skill had been to doze off just when an argument between the two grew heated, as they most often had. It had been insufferable then. She would not stand for it now!

Pivoting sharply, she stalked to the side of the sofa. "Oh no, you don't! No sleeping in my house!"

A lazy eye opened in amusement. "None? What do *you* do for rest?"

With a sigh of exasperation at the manipulation of her words, she threw her hands up. "I give up. What is it you want? Why are you here?"

The force of the gray orbs now held her. "We didn't have enough time this afternoon."

"Please, Senator. It's almost eleven. This is no time to discuss anything. I'm exhausted and you look half-asleep yourself." Half-asleep and half-awake; it was the latter that suddenly alarmed her more than the former.

Lithely he drew himself to a seated position. "You're right. Let's get to it. Come over here."

Standing no more than five feet from where he sat, Daran prayed that he could not hear the thunderous pounding of her heart. It shook even her with its sudden intensity. Drawing on what meager poise remained in the storehouse of her life's experience, she pushed her hands into her pockets and stepped sideways into a more casual stance. Her eyes held his, not from desire, but from helplessness.

"Come on," he repeated softly, cocking his head to the side.

"Wh-what?"

This time he merely pointed a strong forefinger toward the cushion beside him. In other circumstances it might have been an innocent request. There was, in this instance, however, no innocence in the eyes that lured her, in the coiled readiness of his outwardly casual pose. Mutely she stood and stared at him, nonplussed as never before. At the risk of making an utter fool of herself, if his intent was an honorable one, she waited for his next move. It was a maddeningly small one, mammoth in its implication.

Raising his hand again, he crooked the same tan forefinger, ordering her to come to his side. Slowly she shook her head. Both knew precisely what he wanted, but, Daran, for one, could not possibly acquiesce.

It seemed an eternity that he pondered her reluctance. His eyes never left her face, nor did hers leave his. The trembling of her limbs was but a token show of the battle waging within the slender form. Aware of some inner torment, he was fully in ignorance of its cause. Her words did nothing to enlighten him.

"I think you'd better leave now," she whispered softly.

Where she had feared resistance to her suggestion, there was only a loud and exaggerated sigh. "Maybe I'd better," he murmured, rising from the sofa and starting slowly for the door, scooping up his jacket as he passed the chair on which it lay. Dutifully she followed him, showing him out in perfect hostesslike form. That was her mistake. For, at the door, he turned swiftly and unexpectedly, startling her into silence as he seized her shoulders and held her close before him.

A husky drawl sealed her fate. "That's better now. This really was cut much too short this afternoon." For the first time, she understood the full meaning of his banter about unfinished business. The gleam in his eye was unmistakable. He was no different—no different at all!

As fear surged through her veins, she tried to pull from his grasp. The fingers on her shoulders merely tightened their hold, digging mercilessly into her skin. His gaze mirrored that same intensity of feeling, terrifying her all the more.

"Please, Senator . . ." she begged in a whisper, imploring him with every bit of feeling her wide-open amber eyes could convey.

Her plea went unheeded as his eyes moved in a slow caress of her features. As though touched by fire, her cheeks flamed, then her chin, the delicate line of her jaw and her ears, until finally the searing brand came to rest on her lips. Struggling to escape the invisible bond, she pulled back again, only to be hauled in closer this time on the rebound.

Again she pleaded with him. "I don't want this. Please, let me go. Just leave." Her breath came in short bursts, her voice sounding weaker by the minute. The hands on her provided the support now that her own shaky legs could not. It was happening—it was happening all over again.

Then something different occurred. Slowly and subtly the fine line between fear and excitement merged; the two became indistinguishable from one another. As his lips lowered to hers, she vacillated, needing to pull back, wanting to lean forward. Reflexively her hands moved to his arms, maintaining that distance between them, allowing no more.

Pulse racing, she awaited his kiss. But as before, he teased her, moving to within a breath of her, then pausing, brushing his lips against the corner of her mouth, then pulling back. He had to know exactly what effect his toying had on her; his hands could feel the trembling that had little now to do with denial. Yet he continued, determined to evoke a response to his liking.

Within Daran the war still raged on, the lines of battle now clearly drawn between the adversaries—mind and body. As noble as were the standards of the mind, they were doomed. As the sensually powerful onslaught went on, her body very slowly edged closer to his until, finally, her hands eased upward to eliminate the barrier between them.

Only then did his lips capture hers in full domination, devouring them with a hunger indicative of the backfire effect of his own teasing. One hand slid along her spine, curving her body to the lines of his. The other wound through the thick mane of hair at the back of her head to hold it still beneath his kiss. The vortex of his passion was mind-boggling; drawn into its core, she surrendered to the flames that licked at her nerve endings and heated the blood within.

When his lips gentled on hers, she responded, slowly at first, then with growing conviction as the sense of giving heightened her own momentary bliss. It was something she had never experienced before. Awestruck, she yearned for more. Her long fingers crept from the sinewed strength of his arms to his shoulders, then his neck, thrilling in the warmth that awaited them. But best of all was their arrival at the hard muscles of his back, for, in reaching that far side and holding tenaciously there, she found herself more snugly crushed against his chest, a delightfully safe and heady haven.

Locked in fierce embrace, the two were mindless of the escalation of their kiss. No longer were lips the sole players; now tongues joined in, then teeth as well. It was a kiss that demanded full commitment, one that allowed no equivocation. When it ended, Daran was breathless. If there was any consolation to be had, it was in the ragged gasp of the man now towering above her.

With this temporary release came a resurgence of the old inbred fear. What would he demand next? Lips, moist and passion-rouged, trembled as her eyes looked plaintively up at him. His kiss had robbed her of the strength to resist; would he use that edge to compromise her further?

A frown creased his brow, drawing the lips that moments before had been full and warm and active into a thin hard line. His eyes searched hers in vain; the cause of her fear was a mystery to him, though the shadow that haunted her features was all too real. When, after agonizingly long moments of silence, a gentle smile curved his lips, the breath she had subconsciously held slipped slowly out. His hands fell to her shoulders, her arms, her hands, then dropped to his own sides by way of retreat. With a sideway sweep he retrieved his jacket, fallen victim to their kiss, then straightened a final time.

"I'll be in touch," he murmured, velvet smooth, then turned and let himself out. For a mindless blend of seconds the blank expanse of the vacant doorway held Daran speechless. Then, slowly, clarity returned. In a wild flash of reality Daran sensed that she had just submitted, freely but unknowingly, a résumé of her qualifications to the handsome senator from Connecticut. All that remained was to await his next step. Infuriated with the thought, she was to be obsessed with it through the long and sleepless night ahead. If only she understood what it was he wanted. Her outspoken criticism of his proposed legislation had initially caught his attention; that much was certain. Yet it seemed the last topic he wished to discuss when he was with her. More disturbing even was the suspicion that discussion, in any form, had been far from his mind when he so boldly materialized on her doorstep this evening. If so, she vowed stubbornly, he was in for a disappointment. In truth, after long hours of brooding on the matter, she had to admit that there was a definite biological attraction between them. Or rather, *she* reluctantly admitted the undeniable fact of his utterly virile magnetism. From *his* point of view, she was one of many, by all imaginable estimates. The responsibility, if such was the case, fell on her shoulders to rechannel his energies toward those others by her own refusal to play the game. Recalling how mindlessly her own response to him had surged forth earlier that evening, she feared her task to be easier said than done.

The battle resumed early the next morning as the weight of exhaustion fought the bright yellow shards of sunlight that streamed into Daran's room. Turning her head to the pillow, the events of the day before awakened her consciousness as the glaring daylight had not done. The soft coverings of her bed bore the brunt of her frustration, thrown back in a fit of annoyance as she stalked toward the bathroom.

To arise with such agitation was foreign to her. Disgusted with herself for being so affected by her encounter with Drew Charles, she showered, breakfasted, then, dressed in a halter top and shorts, made her way to the garden to work off her distress in the cool clumps of moist earth to be overturned. The spring air held a lingering chill. Gradually, with the vehemence of her work, her goosebumps disappeared as did the worst of her temper. In an instant of renewal she pushed all thought of the senator from her mind, forcing attention to the more urgent matters facing her on Monday. In this she was only partly successful. For, with the predictability of a pre-set alarm, the phone rang promptly at ten.

A wan smile broke at the corners of her mouth. Every Sunday morning it came, as sure as the fist-thick wad of *Hartford Courant* atop her doorstep. In anticipation she had plugged in the patio extension. Now, soil-dusted bare feet covered the smooth flagstone to answer the shrill ring that contrasted so sharply with the sweet song of the red-winged blackbird whose serenade it had interrupted.

"Hello?" She could have as easily begun with a simple "Yes, Mother," for all the question there was as to the caller. When the deeply mature female voice filtered back across the miles to her, she smiled more broadly. Despite the many differences she had had with her mother over the years, her affection was undeniable.

"Daran, sweetheart! How are you?" Mary Abbott missed her only child. And, seasoned as she was at disguising her emotions, the subtle lilt in her voice—though it

66

rarely lasted past the initial interchange between the two —was a giveaway.

"I'm fine, Mother. And you?"

"Not bad, for an old lady," she quipped in usual form. For a woman of just fifty, she was as young and energetic as they came.

As always, and as was expected, Daran rebuked her. "Mother, you are certainly *not* an old lady." Then, with the dutiful response having been offered, she went on. "How is Hugh?"

"Busy, as always. But, Daran—" her mother broke quickly into what must have been uppermost in her mind, idle greeting having now been forsaken "—it sounds as though *you* are the one who is really busy. Muriel sent us the clippings from the *Courant.*" *Thank you, Muriel Baker,* Daran mused in silent sarcasm. "You are getting quite some attention there. I hadn't realized you were as involved in the case of children's rights."

Calmly and deliberately Daran answered her. "It's my line of work, Mother. The Child Advocacy Project has begun to attract a following. We've just gotten two grants, one from the state, one from a private foundation. It's only natural that the papers should pay us more heed."

"But, *you. You* are their spokeswoman, Daran," the older woman persisted. "The articles portray you well. I knew you couldn't stay out of the fray for long!" It was, on the surface, an innocent statement. Yet the pain of its implication dug into her daughter sharply.

Denial quickly followed the sigh of exasperation on Daran's lips. "Don't be silly, Mother." Her exaggeration of the appellation told of her impatience. Sinking with a tired slump into a nearby deck chair, she elaborated. "I've never been involved in anything like this before. It was never *my* name that reached the papers."

"But you were by his side, supporting him." The soft

excitement in her mother's voice hardened Daran even more.

Her grimace shaped her words. "You've got it all wrong."

"You know, dear—" the other voice lowered slightly "—Hugh is still hoping that you and Bill will get back together. It wasn't all *that* bad, was it?"

That her own mother remained indifferent to the full extent of the suffering her daughter had endured was a great irritant. "It was a hell I hope never to repeat, Mother. I'll be very happy if I never see Bill again." Wasn't that a major reason for shunning Washington? "Listen," she began, struggling for evenness, "I love Hugh. He has been a wonderful husband to you and was a good father to me—" *perhaps a bit pushy and hard-nosed at times* Daran thought "—during the years of my childhood, but I simply can't lead the kind of life that he has chosen for the two of you. You may enjoy the endless dinners and fundraisers and rallies, but I did not."

"You certainly carried it off well," her mother chided, "for someone who supposedly didn't like it."

Had it not been for the happenings of the past twenty-four hours, Daran's patience might have held. As it was, she was tired and edgy. Bitterness was thick on her tongue when she lashed out against her mother's faint accusation. "But, of course! I was trained for years to fit into the political arena. Wasn't that the purpose of dancing school and poise class and all those dinners I was dragged to, not to mention a boarding school of the caliber of Miss Dunham's?"

Stunned momentarily by the force behind her daughter's thoughts, Mary Abbott lapsed into silence, but only momentarily. "Are you never going to marry again?" Wasn't this another of those supposed ideals in life?

"Six months of marriage to Bill Longley was enough to

keep me for the next twenty years, Mother." The bad taste in her mouth had nothing to do with the bits of dirt which had settled on her lip as Daran chewed unconsciously on a fingernail. As a child she had bitten her nails with a fury, resistant to all demands that the habit was both unclean and unladylike. Only in moments of stress, particularly ones involving the past, did the practice recur. Looking down now at the tiny chip on the tip of the longest of her well-shaped nails, Daran was furious. "I'm perfectly happy with my life, for a change." She spoke purposefully, ignoring the half-truth that recent events had made of her words. "And I don't see any need to get married," Daran continued. "It can't offer me anything I don't already have." Periodically her mother went off on this vein; as always, Daran overreacted. If she were to be truthful with herself, there *was* something her life lacked. Love. It was a quantity with which she dealt every day in her work, for the source of so much mental anguish, both in the children with whom she worked, or in adults with whom she did not, was love, its misuse, misinterpretation, even absence. It was this very factor that made her so astute a psychologist; she poured the love into her work which her personal life spared, devoting herself to patients and students with the strength of that undiluted quality. For the time being, at least, she was content with the arrangement. She was her own woman; that seemed to be all that mattered.

Again her mother was oblivious to the depth of her feelings on the subject, choosing to attribute her feistiness to an instinct for self-defense. Boldly she persisted, reminding Daran of precisely why she had, herself, chosen to leave Cleveland so many years ago. "Do you hear from him at all?"

"Bill?"

"Yes, dear. Have you heard from him?"

"No." Unequivocally and mercifully, *no*.

Blithely her mother babbled on. "He hasn't remarried either, you know. We did see him several weeks ago at a party at the Hilton." Wondering if this information was supposed to hold any significance for Daran, she gazed off at the maples skirting the yard, their buds mere hints of lime. Had her mother been before her, she might have yawned for effect. But the other proceeded on a tempting note, as though holding a Hershey bar before a chocolate addict. "He looked very handsome. And he asked for you. I hadn't received these clippings then, but I did tell him a little about your work."

"Mother, you didn't!" Dismay brought Daran up from her feigned lethargy. As a finger moved reflexively to her mouth, she thrust it angrily behind her back.

"It's no harm, dear. He was interested."

"I'll bet." It had been the supreme blow to Bill's overinflated ego when Daran had left him, then, horror of horrors, filed for divorce. If for no other reason than that abysmal pride, he would take her back in a minute.

Then her mother paused as a new thought crossed her mind with fleeting urgency. "He's still sending you money, isn't he?" Whether it was maternal concern or the hope that some small link still existed between the two that prompted Mary Abbott's question, Daran couldn't say. Not that it mattered; the question had a very simple answer.

"I suppose he is. The lawyers handle that lovely matter." For an instant, the months of bickering until, ironically, her stepfather, Hugh, had interceded to settle the matter of alimony, returned with all their unpleasantness. Bill had fought the divorce to the end—quietly, of course, and in the total confidence of the lawyer's offices. It had only been Hugh's final plea, framed in terms of Bill's own political career, that had turned the tide. Everything had been hushed, as it was to this day.

70

"What do you mean, you suppose he is. It's your bank account, isn't it?" There had been times when, as exemplified by this protectiveness now, Daran had suspected that, had it not been for her mother's supreme devotion to her husband and the limelight they shared, she would have sided wholeheartedly with her daughter in this ugly matter. But those times had been too few and far between to give them full credence.

"Mother," she explained a final time, "I do not keep track of it. I am not interested. In the five years we've been apart, I have not touched one cent of that money. I told you I wouldn't, and I meant it. Fortunately, thanks to the money that came to me from Father's trust when I turned twenty-one, I have never needed anything. Now I can support myself." Suddenly the conversation was more than Daran wanted to handle on this Sunday morning. "And speaking of which, I have a meeting in an hour or so." She lied. "So I'd better go and get dressed. I'll talk with you next week?" The pattern repeated itself all too often. When the give-and-take with her mother reached a dead end, Daran feigned an excuse to sever it. Inevitably she was swamped with guilt soon after.

Miraculously Mary Abbott took the hint. "Of course, dear," she murmured with an unusually genuine sigh. "Take care of yourself, now, and, Daran—" She hesitated, suddenly unsure of herself.

"Yes, Mother?"

"Do call me if you feel like talking. It gets very . . . lonesome . . . out here sometimes."

Taken totally off guard by the poignant plea, Daran could only muster a soft, "I will," before she hung up the phone. Then, to her dismay, she burst into tears. It was the first truly spontaneous confession, indirect as it was, that her mother had ever made to her. Perhaps Daran was the selfish one. Perhaps her mother, despite all pretenses,

71

did have some needs that were unfulfilled. Daran was her only child; they were so far from each other both physically and emotionally. Would things ever be different? Now that Daran was a mature woman in her own right, perhaps the two could find some common ground on which to unite. Sniffing, she stopped to ponder how she would handle her own children one day—then the true emptiness set in. Would there ever be any children upon whom Daran could shower that intuitive mother-love which was a part of her? Would there ever be a man for whom she could feel a very different, but equally as all-abiding love? It seemed an open-ended question, one which she could in no way come close to answering. Rather, with a vow to take the initiative and phone her mother herself, perhaps later in the week when her own emotions had steadied, she returned to the garden and its therapeutic demands.

"The same fellow has just called again, Dr. Patterson." The soft voice of MaryAnne Steubings filtered through Daran's preoccupation with a problem posed by one of the students in her morning seminar. Halting, then retracing several steps to the secretary's desk, she looked down at the pink call slip which the young student had just written out.

A puzzled frown curved down lips whose gloss had faded through the morning's lecture. "I haven't been in all morning. Were there other calls from this—" she studied the handwritten name closely, its sound unfamiliar—"Mr. Morrow?"

"Oh, yes," MaryAnne affirmed, her eyes widening dramatically. "I got in no more than an hour ago, and there had already been three calls. And that was at eleven! He's called twice since then."

Morrow. Morrow. The name had a familiar ring as she said it once more, yet she could not place it. With a sigh, she crammed the thin slip of paper between her books and her blazer, then paused as MaryAnne leaned closer, a conspiratorial glint in her eye.

"His name is Stanley Morrow . . . and he's from Senator Charles's Hartford office. It's written in large print all over the other messages," she offered in quiet explanation and subtle apology for having caught sight of them, "so I didn't think I needed to repeat it here. He was quite vehement that you should know where to find him." The good humor in her eyes remained there; she had sufficient respect for her employer to know when to be still.

Whatever it was that passed through Daran's features in the interim remained a mystery to MaryAnne. For when the professor turned back to her, there was nothing but composure. "Were there any other messages for me?"

The younger woman shook her head. "Oh, Mrs. Melanson did ask me, before she left to go to lunch, to remind you about that final exam for the seniors. It has to be in for typing by the end of the week."

Thought of the work which had been thwarted on Saturday glimmered in memory. With a sigh, Daran straightened. "Thanks, MaryAnne. I'll get it to her."

Moments later, the efficient Dr. Patterson was behind her desk, nibbling absently at the tuna on whole wheat she had picked up on the run in the cafeteria moments earlier. Twice she cleared her throat and reached for the telephone. Twice she hesitated, then returned to the sandwich. Finally, disgusted at her lack of courage, she thrust the half-eaten lunch to the side of the desk, stormed to the long metal bookshelf which held her hospital notebooks, grasped one angrily, and slammed it on the desk. What did they want now? The senator had already left his orders; what did the henchman want? If she was lucky, the only person other than MaryAnne, Mrs. Melanson, the regular department secretary, knew of the calls. But that was too optimistic a prospect, knowing as she did the kindly woman's propensity for gossip. Surely the entire department knew of the calls, not to mention the secretaries from other departments; it was only a matter of time before the entire school knew that Daran Patterson was to be working with the state's junior senator.

The jangle of the telephone echoed in every cell of Daran's being. There was no excuse for ignoring it. Amber eyes fell with reluctance on the offending instrument as a slim and unsure hand reached for it. Mercifully it was Glen Roberts.

"Daran, Lois just informed me that she was going to do some late shopping tomorrow, since I have to work. How about joining me for a bite to eat before the meeting?"

Relief mixed with pleasure in her response. "That sounds great, Glen. Where should I meet you?"

"Why don't you drive to my office, then we can take it from there. About six?"

"Fine."

It was a simple enough exchange of words. Only when she thought back on it later did Daran begin to wonder. An hour-and-a-half bite to eat before the meeting—it could mean only one thing. Glen, too, was bidden by curiosity to hear of her meeting with Senator Andrew Charles. It seemed that everyone was smitten with the man and his power. Everyone, that was, except Daran.

Daran gathered her things together and left immediately for the hospital, bent on pushing the devil from her mind by an afternoon of intent concentration on the private patients she would be seeing. The tactic worked. Yet the problem remained, as she was quick to discover on her return to the college later that afternoon.

"Daran?" The bright smile of the department chairman, Hamilton Brody, emerged from behind the half-closed door of her office soon after she entered it. "Can I

74

speak with you for a minute?" The robust figure moved forward; response was unnecessary.

Daran liked Hamilton. Not only was he well-read, well-spoken, and well-respected in the field, but it had been his firm recommendation that the school hire her in the first place. The two had gotten along from the start. A warm smile lit her face in the belated invitation which words had not offered. "Sure, Ham. I always have time for you. You know that." A good twenty years older than Daran, the man's surprising shyness brought out a certain protective instinct in her, one which softened her response to him all the more. In the short time she had known him, he had become a kind of father figure, appealing for both his brilliance and his reserve.

An apologetic smile twisted his lips to the side of his round, ruddy face. "They're after *me,* now, Daran. You've got to get back to them!"

"What are you ever talking about?" Nervously she fingered the corner of her blotter; already she suspected the answer.

"The senator's office—they've been calling all day. That fellow, Stanley Morrow, can be very persistent. He wants to speak with you as soon as possible."

A long, slow breath filtered through Daran's lips as she sought to control her temper. "I'm sorry, Ham. There was no need for you to be bothered." Eyes studied the soft cuff of her pink blouse as it edged from the sleeve of her tan blazer, hiding as much as possible from her companion the dilemma she faced. He, too, however, was curious.

"I know that you had a meeting with the senator on Saturday about the Child Advocacy Project and his Rights of Minors Act. What is it they want now?"

"I only wish I knew." The words escaped on impulse. Daran shot a quick glance at the man opposite her before lowering her eyes once more. "He wants me to do some work for him in Washington this summer. I assume that's what this Morrow is calling about." Whether her earlier slip had been covered, she did not know. Quickly she chattered on. "I've had a hectic day and it's far from over. I'll give this fellow a ring in a few minutes; if he's not in, I'll just have to speak to him in the morning."

Hamilton Brody shook his head gently from side to side. "He won't like that. It sounded as though his patience was beginning to wear thin when he called me just before you came in."

Daran's own patience waned. "That's his problem, not ours. I'm only sorry that he disturbed you. I will try him now, Ham. Thanks for tipping me off. These politicians and their aides can be royal pains at times."

A gray-tipped eyebrow, bushy in contrast to his bald head, rose in surprise. "You sound as if you've had prior experience."

Relaxation had always been natural with this gentleman; today was no exception. "My stepfather has been into politics for years. You could say I was weaned on it."

"Does he hold office now?"

Dark waves bobbed about her shoulders as she shook her head. "No. As a matter of fact, he has never been the office-holder, merely the man behind who pulls the strings." Her smile succeeded in softening the harsh implication of her words. "He is a major fundraiser for the state committee back in Ohio. I'm really very proud of him. His hard work behind the scenes has resulted in much of the progressive action in the state over the last years."

"And now you're following in his footsteps?" The soft voice and its words startled her. Was this eminent psychologist correct in his analysis? Is that what she herself was doing with her own work—and those press interviews which she was fast coming to regret?

76

"No, sir!" It was a vehement denial aimed as much at herself as at Hamilton Brody. Yet she was to spend much time pondering the possibility in the days ahead.

Mercifully Stanley Morrow was not in his office when she finally got around to calling later that afternoon. Soon after, she left the office to catch a light supper before crossing the campus to attend a rescheduled class of the modern-dance group that she had joined several months earlier. The exercise was potent medicine for her taut muscles, the pleasant company of the ten other women equally as restorative. When several of them invited her to a local coffee house for a snack after the class, she gladly accepted. Ranging in occupation from housewife to fashion designer, her fellow dance enthusiasts were an interesting and diversionary group. The time they spent around the small, dark corner table passed all too quickly for Daran, whose days were so packed with work that she rarely made time for the cultivation of leisure friendships. Here, however, she was accepted as one of the group, and she opened up accordingly, offering her share of anecdotes of on-campus happenings, joining the others in hysterical laughter at someone else's light-hearted rejoinder. Reassured by the prospect of seeing these women next week on Wednesday night, she finally dragged herself from the warm group and headed home.

The face of her watch read eleven o'clock when, back in Simsbury, she closed her front door behind her. Exhausted, she fell promptly into a sound sleep, blissfully ignorant of the repeated peal of her telephone while she had been out, and equally as ignorant of the caller who grew more and more impatient. It was only natural, therefore, that his entrance the following morning would be an exaggerated one.

It was barely 8:45. Sipping slowly at a cup of hot coffee, Daran ran through some notes for her morning class,

77

enjoying the relative quiet of her office at this hour. Absently she traced the large curve of an earring as she leaned back in her seat, a soft smile on her face. Academia rushed nowhere; aside from those of her colleagues who had early classes, the rest straggled in to the department in random and unpredictable sequence. Daran was the odd one of the bunch, up early and at her desk, running from appointment to appointment, cramming her days full. She was a doer; perhaps Hamilton Brody had been right in his analysis of her.

The muffled sound of voices, growing louder and more distinct by the minute, a steady drum roll approaching with frightening speed, brought her back from her musings. The slender body straightened instinctively. Amber eyes shot to her door as it opened to reveal a group of no less than four people, three men and one woman, poised on the threshold. The fact that she had never laid eyes on any one of them was irrelevant; Daran knew immediately who they were.

"Dr. Patterson?" the man in front, the leader-apparent, began. "I'm Stanley Morrow. I manage the Hartford office of Senator Charles. May we come in?" He was good-looking and tall, the most impressive of the group, yet Daran suspected, in the instant, that this one would have paled sadly had the senator, himself, been around.

As though buoyed by this thought in her imminent discourse with his underling, Daran found the composure she needed. "By all means, please do." Her eye skimmed the other three for a brief and cursory instant, during which she assumed them to be local staffers, from the uniform crispness of their dress and the aura of gameful participation which suffused their bright features. This other was, for the time being, their overseer, and they seemed perfectly happy to function beneath his whip. The others now made themselves more evident, following the

78

forefinger that ordered them, silently but definitively, to follow him into the small office. Daran could not contain her amusement when the last of the four, the woman, slithered gracefully behind the others to the side of the room. It was as though each was to study her closely while the leader spoke. But it was Daran, emboldened, strangely, by the more intimate time she had spent with the senator several nights before, who spoke first.

"What can I do for you, Mr. Morrow? I'm sorry I've missed your calls. Unfortunately my schedule is particularly hectic at this time of year."

It became immediately clear to her that the man did not forgive her even one of those futile phone calls. His annoyance was etched in the muscles which tightened at his jaw, and in the taut band of skin on either side of his nose. But control was the thing in his line of work.

"You are, indeed, a difficult woman to reach. But," he quipped with a pasted smile that failed to move beyond the harsh curve of his mouth, "if Mohammed won't come to the mountain, as the saying goes . . ." His words trailed off, those unspoken ones well taken. Daran ignored them; she could play the game as well.

"What can I do for you?" she repeated gently.

"Senator Charles insisted that we keep in touch with you on the Rights of Minors business. He wants you to know that we are here to give you any assistance you may need in researching or compiling your position paper." His use of the we was token, as the others appeared unable to speak, move, or do anything besides stare at her.

"That's a very kind offer." She thanked him, purposely including the others in the spread of her vision. "But I believe I can handle everything myself. My own thoughts are quite well-formulated on the issue of children's rights; it's what I work with so much of the time." The invasion was beginning to irk her, knowing as she did of the forty-odd students who would be awaiting her arrival in the lecture hall within the next five minutes. "I do appreciate your gesture. If there's anything I can think of for you to do, I'll give you a call." Would they take the hint and leave?

She had made the mistake of taking Stanley Morrow at face value. Obviously he had more on his mind than a simple offer of his assistance. "One other thing, Dr. Patterson. I know that you must be busy right now—" the gist of his lip service fell flat beneath the hardness of his glance "—but I would like to mention the press. Watch out for them. They can be quite skillful in turning words around to most powerfully attract attention. If you would like, I could easily arrange to be with you whenever you meet with the press on this issue."

At last the purpose of his visit was clear. Anger welled within her, but was barely hidden by the thin mask of indulgence when she finally responded. "Again, I appreciate your concern. I believe that I know what to expect from the press. Actually, so far, they have interpreted my comments quite accurately." The smug grin that had made its appearance quickly disappeared as she went on more soberly. "If you are asking that I restrain my criticism of Senator Charles, I'm afraid I cannot comply. I do believe very strongly that his bill is a beginning; it's up to people like me to convince the senator to take it further." The hardened expression on the face opposite her told her that her assumption had been correct; he had come to mollify her. The only thing that riled her more at that moment was the thought that Andrew Charles had put him up to it.

"In the end, Dr. Patterson, your own cause could be hurt if its image becomes one of extremism." The warning note in his voice was unmistakable.

Incensed, she stood silent for a moment. Then, with a

deliberateness born of years in the political arena, she began to gather up the books and papers for her class. "If that is a threat, Mr. Morrow," she ventured calmly, "I will just have to risk it. My cause is a good one; I'm prepared to fight for it. Now, you'll have to excuse me—" she gestured with an impulsive shooing motion toward the door "—I've got to leave. My class begins in—" her arm brought its watch into view "—two minutes. I'd rather not be late."

Reluctantly the group parted to let her through. There were no trite words of farewell to follow her down the hall; neither did she offer anything herself. It was all she could do to curb her irritation and make her exit as smooth as she willed it. The composure was all at surface level; beneath, annoyance reigned.

It was not to be eased when, later that day, the inevitable showdown came with Glen Roberts. In his own gently forceful way, he would be put off no longer. Hedging wherever possible, Daran related to him the brief course the meeting had taken that Saturday as well as the unexpected and unwelcome visit of the troops that morning. Noticeably absent in her report was any mention whatsoever of that other encounter, the one at her home on Saturday night. Her justification was that it had had nothing to do with either the Rights of Minors Act or her Child Advocacy Project. In reality, it had not, and that fact continued to perplex her.

Respite from contact with Senator Charles was elusive. Wednesday morning the calls from Stanley Morrow resumed. This time, and with as much curtness as she could get away with, Daran returned the call promptly, floored by the pert demands—politely phrased as requests —for her resume, a short bio on her, and a photograph.

"What on earth do you need a picture for?" she had asked in dismay. Against her will, it sounded as though she was getting herself deeper into something by the minute, though that something was a mystery to her.

The voice on the other end of the line had been suitably patronizing. "Oh, it's just a formality. We like to have these things on file, should we need them at some point. And particularly with a woman as attractive as you are, the publicity never hurts."

She had ignored both the unsought compliment and the crux of his words, choosing, rather, to focus for the moment on the final exam that begged to be finished. With deadlines in sight, there was no choice, mercifully. The requests of the senator's home office were quietly filed behind the myriad more important things that occupied Daran's mind; they would wait, she reasoned, until the proper motivation struck her.

Subsequent phone calls from the persistent Mr. Morrow did nothing on that score. Each time, she assured him quietly that she would get something to him as soon as it was humanly possible. To her own amazement, she felt little guilt at the deception. The facts of a resume, a biography, and a photo were unimportant compared to the matter at the core of it all, the issue of children's rights. On that vein, these local staffers were as helpless as she. It was the biggest fish that would either nourish the children or overturn the boat. Subconsciously she waited for him to nibble at the bait she offered.

CHAPTER 4

For two weeks she heard nothing. To her chagrin the frequent references to the senator, both in the papers and on television, attracted more of her attention than it had in the past. Not only was she unusually interested in everything he said—and none of it dealt with the Rights of Minors Act—analyzing his positions on the various issues, but her eye remained glued to every image of the man, comparing it with her own perception, then chiding herself accordingly when her own surpassed the other each and every time. With no further word from his office— *could they have given up so easily?* she wondered—and clear indication from the media coverage that the senator was part of a Congressional delegation on a fact-finding mission in Central America for the week, she relaxed in the knowledge that, while nothing positive could be done until he returned, nothing negative could happen either. The cynicism of the past was the dominant emotion guiding her approach to the senator. Whether she would indeed be working with him this summer remained to be seen. Though she would not go to Washington, there did appear to be several advantages to an agreement with him for some type of collaboration. His bill had not yet gone to committee; there would still be hearings, with witnesses and senators alike speaking on the merits and faults of the legislation. If she, in some small way, could influence the senator who had sponsored the bill at the start, the bill might be just that much stronger. Arrogance played no role at all in her reasoning; only the firm belief in her cause steadied her for the long, uphill climb.

Having spent a full two hours of vigorous physical movement, a climb of any kind, aside from that into a long, hot tub, was the furthest thing from her mind when she pulled the VW up to the house that Wednesday night. She hadn't even bothered, with the weather warming in this first week of May, to change from her leotards and tights following her modern dance class. Rather, she had simply thrown the thigh-long sweater-jacket she had worn to school that morning over her shoulders as she ran from the gym to her car. This she pulled close about her as she climbed out now to eye the sporty silver Cimarron which stood, parked, before her front door. In another situation, particularly had the vehicle been a battered pick-up truck, she might have been alarmed. But this small, late-model Cadillac bore a low number plate and another, more unusual insignia, one which, in the darkness, she could not quite distinguish, but which spoke of some type of membership to something other than the State Penitentiary Inmates' Association.

"Hello?" she called toward the car, intent on determining the identity of her mysterious caller. When no answer came, she slowly approached the silver door, gleaming now in the full moonlight. The car was empty. Instantly her eye flew to the front door, half hidden in shadow as the narrow overhang filtered the moonbeams randomly. There, distinct yet dark, was a tall form, relaxed back against the stucco surface of the house, just beside its door. Unsure, though not frightened, she waited for some sign that the figure saw her. It came in a low and tired flow of inexplicably exciting words.

"In another few minutes, I'd have been asleep on your

doorstep. That would have been quite a thing for you to find when you returned. Where have you been so late? It's nearly ten o'clock." To her surprise, there was no indignance in his tone, but rather an unexpected concern which was too soft and sweet to ignore.

"I have a dance class every Wednesday night. It's over at nine-thirty. I came directly." Her heart was racing, though she certainly hadn't run all the way. Now, as the dark figure stepped forward into the moonlit drive to which she had been rooted, she wished she had; at least, then, there might have been a plausible explanation for the thudding of her heart. "I-I thought that you were out of the country." It was the first and only thing that came to mind.

The deep intonation was smooth and soothing, despite the fatigue it reflected. "I was. We returned this evening. I wanted to stop . . . home, before I returned to Washington. It was a tiring trip." That went without saying.

"Why don't you come in?" The offer came of its own accord, totally naturally. "I'll make us a cup of coffee."

Running the short distance back to her car, she retrieved her pocketbook, books, and the clothes she had worn that morning, only then realizing that the outfit she wore outlined her every curve. The shadows held her blush in confidence as she fumbled for her keys, then extended them to Drew as she flipped the car door shut with the force of one slim hip. The lights were ablaze in the front hall and living room by the time she entered. Had she been worried, however, about the provocation of her costume, it had been needless. Without a word the senator proceeded to the sofa, sank down on it, lay back his head, and closed his eyes, exhausted.

Dropping her things in a chair, Daran escaped to the kitchen, put on some coffee, retreated to her bedroom to put on a more conservative pair of slacks and a blouse, 'then returned to the living room, having taken the coffee-pot and two cups from the kitchen. This time, however, there was no mistaking it. He was sound asleep, sprawled exactly as he had been when she left him, making no movement upon her reappearance. The full-cushioned armchair opposite him easily took her meager weight when, having placed the second cup on the coffee table, she sat down with her own, sipping slowly as she studied the man before her.

It was a unique opportunity. His tawny eyelashes made no flicker. His breathing was as steady as hers was not. With the luxury of leisure, her golden eyes absorbed the vision. His legs were long, one flexed at the knee, one straight, both lean and muscular as suggested by the mold of his charcoal gray slacks. His chest was as broad as she remembered it, the cuffs of his shirt were rolled to the elbow to tempt her with forearms that bore a manly smattering of hair of the same sun-bleached gold that she had seen on the backs of his hands. His face was a picture of relaxation, all tension gone, leaving a serene blend of suntan and the barest hint of a five o'clock shadow. The features were strong—eyes, nose, and mouth—yet strangely vulnerable at rest like this. The casual swath of hair that half-covered his forehead was lighter than it had been, bleached at scattered points by the heat of the Central American sun.

He was rugged yet handsome, virile and commanding; even in sleep, he mesmerized her. Sitting deeper into her chair, she tried to steady her breathing. Yet, looking at the form on her sofa rendered that task impossible. It was that biological attraction she had already recognized, and she could do nothing to blunt its force. A strange knot of emotion gripped her throat; swallowing, she willed it away. The faint tremor in her limbs was another matter.

Helpless to move, she could only sit and stare at the man asleep on her sofa.

Minutes passed and the coffee in both cups cooled as she pondered the situation. In its entirety, it was an enigma. At best she could look at one moment to try to understand it. Strangely the tall and handsome man bore no resemblance to the senatorial presence others would have expected. For the second time now, he had appeared, on the spur of the moment, at her door. At the first, surprise and puzzlement had overwhelmed her. This time was different. Bizarre as was the scene, it seemed perfectly natural to her, that she should be waiting, watching, while Drew Charles slept. He was a man, and she found herself attracted to him as such. His work was another matter; but that had no relevance here.

As though awoken by the intensity of her thought process, he moved his head to the side, lifted a sinewed forearm to shade his eyes from the bright light in the room, then paused in mid-air, recalling at that moment exactly where he was. Slowly the sandy head turned toward her; slowly warm gray eyes reached out to her. A smile, soft and gentle, greeted her.

"Hi." His voice had the force of a roar in its low whisper, tingling through her as she watched his awakening intently. "Sorry about that," he murmured, though making no move to straighten or sit up. Rather, his gaze enveloped her in a snug cocoon. When he extended a hand in silent invitation, she had no choice but to accept it. The sureness of his grasp drew her down to sit on the edge of the sofa by his waist, her body turned sideways to face him. Unbelievably she was more comfortable than she had been before.

"How long did I sleep?" he asked, peering at his watch through sleepy eyes.

"Only about forty-five minutes. You must have been

worn out. Was it a good trip?" Conversation was simpler than she had ever imagined, the words flowing spontaneously.

"Was it a good trip?" He shrugged faintly as he repeated her question. "I suppose it was. We met with diplomats and presidents and all sorts of other dignitaries. The usual smiles were exchanged and handshakes given. We were carted around to see the extent of progress in the various countries. And now we're back. Yes, it was a good trip. I learned a great deal. As to how useful, in the long run, that information will be, I can't say." The note of futility in his last sentence discouraged her, as did the shadows that lingered beneath his eyes, nearly hidden among the sun-streaked lines radiating from their corners, but visible nonetheless.

"Will you get a chance to rest now?"

"Right now," he confirmed with a grin. "And tomorrow morning. By noon, it's back to work."

Daran was aware of the hand that now curved around her waist, as his other continued to hold her own. If sex appeal was the term, the man had it. His presence cast over her a hypnotic spell, such that few thoughts could infiltrate the delicious feeling of peace that surrounded her. Her free hand itched to touch the lips that still held in the barest hint of a smile as he looked at her for a time that seemed infinite. Knowing she should say something, words escaped her. Entranced, she could do nothing but await his move. It was barely perceptible, the airiest shift of his hand from her waist to the curve of her spine, then to her neck, where it tangled in the mass of waves by her ear. When the pressure came gently, she acceded to it, allowing him to guide her head lower until their lips met in a soft, slow kiss. A shudder of excitement passed through her as it deepened gradually, pulling her into its force, sparking a response from her which quickly caught up with his in intensity.

His other hand released hers to travel the length of her arm, caressing the soft curve of her shoulder for but a minute before inching its way along the sensitive cord of her neck to mirror the first in its splay along the side of her head. She could not have lifted her head had she wanted to; his long fingers possessed it with merciful tenderness as his lips continued their soul-reaching kiss. She was breathless when he finally drew her back to look upon her flushed cheeks and soft lips. She was devastated when his eyes lingered on her own, tormenting her with the cushioned offer of their warm gray depths. Desirous only of recapturing the pleasure of the kiss that had ended, it was Daran's head that now lowered, her lips that parted, her hands that journeyed the length of his chest to his shoulders and neck, then wound into the sandy fullness of his hair.

Sensual shock waves reverberated from one fingertip to the other as the heat of passion fanned out from her core to warm every inch of her. Never in her life had Daran been as aroused by a kiss; never had she ached as unconscionably for more. Reading her need, he touched her, a gentle hand circling her breast with deliberate slowness, building her pitch of arousal higher than before, driving her mad with frustration when his finger caressed the erotic nub, its pebbled peak responding instantly. Mindless amid the sensual eddy, she arched closer to him. A soft sigh of delight was her only protest when the buttons of her blouse gave way to his expert touch and the soft material fell to the side.

In a flash of movement, she found herself beneath him, pinned by the line of his thighs. His lips caressed her, his tongue racing fire down her neck as his hand released the catch of her bra, then moved to touch the creamy skin beneath. So lost was she in the pleasure of the moment, a pleasure that had been denied her woman's body for far too long, that she was oblivious to the fact that he had lifted her from the sofa, his lips drugging her further as he carried her toward the room at the far end of the hall, the one lit, her bedroom. It was the feeling, abruptly returned, of time and place and identity, as her head touched the pillow and the looming form lowered itself over her, that triggered her resistance.

"Wait! P-please!" Whether it was the fact of a bed and its implications that shattered the web of primitive response, Daran would never know. In a wave of horror came other images of a bed and a man and the pain she had suffered, both physically and emotionally. "Stop!" she whispered hoarsely, temporarily confusing the time and place as she fought a rising panic.

Beneath the scrutiny of a bewildered silver-eyed gaze, the fact of her terror was inescapable. "What is it, Daran?" Drew asked softly. "What are you afraid of?"

The sound of his voice positively identified the man with her now, yet her fear persisted. He had seen hint of it before; never would he have expected as sharp a mushrooming, however, of something that seemed so out of place in this day and age. Levering himself farther from her, and astonished by his ability to do so when the height of his own arousal was so acute, he pondered the beauty of the face below, drained now of color and shot with tension.

Once again he sought an explanation. "Please tell me. What upset you? You were as eager as I was, until . . ." His let his words die out as she turned her taut face toward the pillow and threw an arm across it defensively. Silence held them frozen for several moments. Finally, with a soft oath, he pushed himself from the bed and left the room.

90

Daran lost track of time as she lay quietly, spent of emotion, weary to the bone. Hadn't she wanted nothing but a long, hot bath? What had she gotten instead? A long, warm body, laced with virility, scented likewise, and eager to engulf her totally, had she allowed it. It had been so beautiful for a while there, a heady and wonderful sense of unity, a oneness of desire. But that was the apex; it could go no higher, no further. Drew Charles was a politician. There was no room for romance in his life. Lust, yes. Passion, yes. Basic physical satisfaction, yes. But romance, no. Future, no. Love, no. She had been through it before; she was an expert. And Bill's brand had left its mark, exerting itself tonight when, for the first time since she had left him more than five years ago, she might have succumbed to the lure of a man. A bitter kind of gratitude filled her but failed to touch the emptiness she felt within.

Most noticeable amid the silence that filtered in from the rest of the house was the absence of the sound of the door closing behind the senator. Intuitively Daran knew that he remained, waiting, in the living room. Resigned to face the music, she rose from the bed, straightened her clothing, and ventured forward.

The broad back at the far end of the room held no hint of his mood, yet the low bend of the fair head, the firm grip of the hands on his hips, the wide stance of his lean legs all suggested a tension which she knew had to exist. One simply did not tempt a man as she had done, albeit unwittingly, then turn from him and expect patience and understanding, particularly with a man of the stature of Senator Andrew Charles, who doubtless had experienced few such turndowns. There would be a minimum of compassion.

Overwhelmed by these thoughts and the untenable situation in which she found herself, Daran stood for several moments at the doorway. The legs that finally carried her forward were less sure than the mind, which only knew that something had to be said to finally conclude the fiasco.

"Senator—" she began, only to be cut off abruptly by the harsh growl which corrected her.

"Drew!" In light of what had taken place earlier, his anger was justified. Yet this short outburst was a mere sample.

"I'm sorry . . . Drew." Her whisper was heartfelt, drawing him around to face her. His features were taut, his eyes a chilled charcoal. To her astonishment, however, when he spoke, his voice retained the calmness of other times.

"Are you all right now?" The eyes that studied hers carefully saw none of the terror that had seized her before. Her confirmation came instantly.

"Yes." With his apparent control, she did feel fine.

"What happened, Daran?" he asked patiently.

But he had been there; surely he knew. Was this some new kind of word game he played? Bewildered, she gazed up at him in silent questioning. Realizing her confusion, he spoke again.

"No, I mean before. Something must have happened before in your life to give you that wounded-dog complex. Every time I get close to you and you allow yourself to respond, it appears. What is it?"

"Nothing." She lied softly. She barely knew the man, senator or not. This was not the time to tell her life story, when it was so very, very private.

But Drew was not about to let it drop. "Nothing?" A tawny brow arched skeptically. "You're a beautiful woman. And I know that you find me . . . attractive." There was no smugness in his suggestion, but she lashed out defensively.

"And thoroughly arrogant!"

The gray eyes did not flicker. "Perhaps arrogant. But that doesn't negate the fact that each time I touch you, you

92

tremble." Unable to deny his claim, she merely averted her eyes, lowering them to fall to the tanned skin exposed by the opened buttons of his light blue shirt. It was an error; true to his words, even taking them one step further, that now familiar tremor flitted about her insides. Dropping her eyes, she focused on the plush carpeting by her feet. With the determination that was part of his unique character, Drew prodded on.

"If it weren't for the heat of your response at the start, I might wonder if you were frigid."

Her dark head shot up. "I'm not."

"No." He smiled softly, pleased at finally receiving a definitive answer. Directness appeared to work. "And, in this day, with your looks, I find it hard to believe that you have reached the age of thirty with your virginity intact."

Indignantly she corrected him. "Twenty-nine."

Again the smile teased the fringe of his lips before disappearing. "Twenty-nine then. But now you're evading the question." The suddenly sharpness of his gaze warned her against that tactic. "Are you a virgin, Daran?"

"No." The word was barely audible. In its wake, an unfathomable expression swept over the carved and manly features towering above her, receding to leave a shade of perplexity in the gray-eyed gaze.

"Then you must have had a bad experience somewhere along the line." When she failed to respond but turned her head away, his patience thinned. Cupping her chin between the lengths of his thumb and forefinger, he forced her face back to his. "Either that," he went on, his voice more icy than she had ever heard it, eyes bearing a similar frost, "or you play a dirty game that no man in his right mind would stand for." The threat was suitably cloaked. She perceived it nonetheless. Cringing inwardly as his hand held her face in its steel grip, she felt her eyes brim with tears.

"I-I wouldn't do that!" she rasped softly, disgusted at the thought of what he had suggested. "I'm not th-that kind of person."

"I didn't think so," he snapped, as angry with himself as with her for forcing the accusation which he had doubted from the start. A jerked movement took his hand from her chin, then himself from the spot, as he paced several yards from her, turned, and pursued the first assumption. Her back was to him, arms wrapped about her middle in distress. "Then you must have been hurt at some point."

Bowing her head, she missed the movement that would have been reflected in the window glass as he approached her. When his hands fell lightly on her shoulders from behind, she jumped in alarm. Doggedly, he held her, turning her around, holding her at arm's length as he repeated his query. "Daran? You've been hurt, haven't you?"

How could she avoid him? His hands held her, his nearness soothed her in such strange ways. In the end persistence would triumph. Why not shorten the agony? Silently her dark head nodded in affirmation. A whispered curse sailed over her head as he drew it gently against his chest, the soft material of his shirt absorbing the few tears that had escaped her moistened eyes. The band of his arms supported her against him and the world outside, until her breathing regained a semblance of steadiness. Only then did he pull back to look into her face, a picture of utter vulnerability.

"I would never hurt you. Don't you know that?" Even amid her own emotional turmoil she detected the hurt in his voice. It puzzled her; was it real, or merely part of the image? As though sensing her indecision, he made a further attempt to calm her, softening his voice to reflect the feeling within him that puzzled him as well. The occasional skittish woman was not unusual; his own reaction to this one was. Though it was none of his business, he felt

94

a surge of anger at the man who had caused her such anguish.

Both thumbs smoothed away the last of the dampness from her cheeks, as he framed her face with his hands. "You're very beautiful, Daran. And passionate. I would find a night with a woman like you very exciting." The musky male scent that filled her senses threatened to arouse that very passion to which he now referred. But the pain of other thoughts remained a tangible intruder, its ghost a hollow at the back of her eyes. Drew picked up on it instantly. "Now don't go all stiff on me again, Daran," he chided gently. "You have to believe that I would never, never cause you pain."

There was pain . . . and there was pain. One was physical, the other psychological. In a moment of foresight she wondered if the danger from this man had more to do with the latter. When finally she spoke, her skepticism was strong. "Why should I believe that, Drew? I hardly know you."

"Oh, come on. Everybody knows me." His words were glib, flowing almost from habit. Their sureness brought back a spark of spirit to her amber eyes, which flashed faintly as they narrowed on him.

"Yes, everybody knows the senator. There's that public image that has to be upheld at all costs. But it's not always true. I know!" To her chagrin, she spilled out more of her feelings than she might have wished. Her bitterness was obvious. Drew noted it, then tabled it for later consideration. His own anger had risen in the face of her reaction to the words which he had so innocently, though wrongly, uttered.

"Look, Daran. I've never hurt a woman in my life. The image, in this case, stands as the truth. And—" he dropped his hands and took a step back "—if you don't believe that, then I'd better leave now." Not one to make idle threats, he let his long legs carry him halfway across the room toward the front door before the force of her voice, strong, clear, and surprising even Daran with its intensity, stopped him.

"No!" The sound softened instantly. "Wait." Slowly he turned. "I do believe it." With inexplicable certainty she did. Yet there was more to say. "It's just that . . . well . . . I really don't know you particularly well." His gaze speared her, daring her to explain herself further. "I know you by reputation only. You were a hard-working and honest representative, and are an outstanding senator. You're—"

"I'm a man." The low roar shook through her, stifling any further praise she may have given. "I don't give a damn about what you think of my record at this particular moment." Thoroughly puzzled as to why he should be so furious, she could only stare as he retraced his steps to face her. "I'm a man. Very sensitive. Very human. And—" he sighed, as though suddenly worn out by the exertion of the argument "—at this point, very tired."

Her softened amber gaze followed him as he once more headed for the door. "You're right," he murmured abruptly, turning. "You really don't know me. But we'll remedy that . . . beginning tomorrow morning. How about breakfast?"

Taken off guard by the sudden change of pace, she stammered. "B-but I have a c-class at ten o'clock—"

"No, I mean an *early* breakfast. I have to be on the plane by then myself. I was thinking more like seven-thirty."

"But it's nearly one o'clock, now . . ." Her eyes widened.

"So?" The lazy slant to his lips took all indifference from his tone, suffusing it with a touch of humor.

Daran nodded, badly in need of that light touch herself. "That's right. I keep forgetting that you politicians don't sleep the way the rest of us do. You catch it when it comes—in the car, at the meeting, on *someone else's sofa* . . ." The emphasis was unnecessary; her point was well taken.

"Touché!" He gave it to her willingly. "So, I'll pick you up at seven-thirty?"

She smiled, suddenly totally relaxed. "Yes."

"Then I'll be on my way." His hand had circled the doorknob before he stopped short, lowered his head, shook it slightly in accompaniment of a soft laugh, then turned, reluctantly, back to her. The grin that covered the distance was nothing less than sheepish. "Ah, Daran . . . ?" he began.

"Yes?"

"I have one slight problem." Still that same grin.

"Problem?" There was something about that grin that sought to warn her.

"I, ah, haven't got anywhere to sleep."

Incredulity underscored her exclamation. "What?"

"I loaned my house to one of my colleagues, Sam Pastori, the senator from Montana. He and his family were to be in the area for the Yale reunion and the festivities that have gone on for much of the week. I didn't expect to return here first when I made the offer."

"That was very generous of you." What else could she say? Intuitively she knew what would come next.

"Would you mind terribly if I spent the night on your sofa? After all, I've already tested it, and it fits."

On the one hand, Daran was furious. So *this* was why he had appeared so suddenly on her doorstep; he had actually planned on spending the night in *her* bed with *her.* But he had changed his tune; for that he deserved some credit. What harm would be done? In light of the boyish innocence that dominated his entire mien at that moment,

97

she knew for certain how he had captured at least a small percentage of his votes. No woman in her right mind could refuse that face. She was no different.

"Oh, all right." She agreed to his proposal with grudging good humor. "But if you want to use the bathroom, you'd better make it fast. I've been promising myself a hot bath since the end of my dance class, and I'd like it within the next five minutes."

The gleam that sizzled from his suddenly warm gray gaze suggested that he would use the bathroom when and for how long he wanted. His words, however, were properly docile. "Of course. I'll just get my bag from the car . . ."

That Daran managed to sleep at all, acutely aware as she was of the man in the room down the hall, was a miracle. Assuming that she would have to awaken him from the deep sleep he would need after his trip, she set her alarm accordingly. To her amazement, however, it was a warm hand on her shoulder that brought her back from her own temporary escape from reality. Having lived alone for so long, she jumped when the slight shaking motion beckoned. Turning with a start, her eyes widened at the sight of the familiar face, apparently wide awake and smiling down at her from his perch on the edge of the bed. Her relief at recognizing him was short-lived. The muscled spread of his chest, bare to the waist, stole her breath a second time.

"Good morning," he crooned softly, no doubt quite comfortable with her reaction. "Did you sleep well?" Nonchalance oozed from the casual inquiry, none of it spreading to her.

"Not bad." Her voice had a husky ring to it. Swallowing convulsively, she cleared her throat to erase its seductive note. But Drew's eyes had fallen to her chest, to the filmy fabric of the nightgown which hid so little from the knowing mind. Before she could protest, he bent to place a light kiss on the hollow at the base of her throat, hesitated for a moment, then lifted his head.

"I'm sorry. I just couldn't resist that." When he showered her with the sweet smile that had now appeared, it was she who could resist nothing.

"That's all right," she whispered in breathy forgiveness, all the while aching to indulge in the pleasure of letting her fingertips play in the soft gold carpet that covered his chest. Though only responding to his natural lure, her own invitation was too much for Drew. Slowly he lowered his lips to taste hers, allowing her hands to satisfy that urge by spreading lightly on the warm skin, sampling the fine-textured surface before climbing to his neck to hold his head closer to her. It was a pattern she could quickly come to know, this mind-blowing masculinity that threw all reason to the winds. Tearing his lips from hers, his hand from its sensual caress of her hip, he straightened.

"I'll take the bathroom first. Don't worry, I won't use the hot water." Laughing both at himself and the dire need for a coolant of some sort, he left the room. Staring after the figure clad in nothing but a pair of old faded blue jeans, she had to marvel. His magnificent physique was one thing, his remarkable self-restraint another. The tingling that remained to tease her lower parts was unmistakable; perhaps she should have given in after all. At some point the fear was bound to fall prey to her desire which, thwarted moments before, now tormented her. What would she do then?

"Daran! You've got twenty minutes!" The deep and flowing growl pushed all other thoughts from mind and she concentrated on dressing for the day. When she emerged from her room ten minutes later, then the bathroom ten minutes after that, she was dressed simply, her full skirt and slim-sleeved blouse, the former in dark brown, the latter in a soft cream color, complementing the busy look that her loose waves, long lashes, pink lips, and freckles comprised. That the flush on her cheeks was authentic, no one had to know but Daran herself.

A fresh and dapper Drew greeted her at the front door, having just returned from replacing his suitcase in the trunk of his car. "All set?" The admiration in his gaze answered his own question. As they left her house, Daran had to admit that he looked stunning. Dressed in a dark suit and light shirt, both miraculously well-pressed—she was later to understand that, as a visiting dignitary, he had been wined and dined and laundered as well—considering the length of his trip, the senator carved a dignified image wherever he went.

The silver Cimarron wound its way smoothly through increasingly rural roads in a direction, to Daran's surprise, away from the city. The silence within was both companionable and pleasant, in sharp contrast to the day that both were sure to have later. When they pulled up before a rustic cabin of sorts by the shore of a small lake, she snapped to attention.

"Where are we?"

Deftly he turned off the engine. "This is where my father lives. We're going to have breakfast with him."

"Your father?" Her first thought was one of treachery. "I *believed* that song and dance about your not having any place to stay last night. Now, here we are at your father's, no more than twenty minutes away."

Undaunted, Drew answered her directly. "In the first place, his cabin is small, as you can see, and he snores like a lumberjack." The twinkle in his eye at the last faded as he went on. "Secondly, we have had our differences over the years. I like to spend time with him—but as little as possible."

100

Daran opened her mouth to argue, then closed it as quickly. Wasn't it the same with her own parents? And why had Drew told her this? For what was not the first time, she suspected that he had revealed to her a part of him that most others never knew. Gracefully she accepted the hand that was offered as she climbed from the car. The scent of the pines and new-budding magnolias assailed her; the soft cushion of fallen pine needles covering the worn stone walkway muffled her high-heeled step as she walked beside the tall and handsome senator.

There was no cause to knock; the door opened even before they reached it. At its jamb stood a man of some seventy years, she imagined, not quite as tall as Drew yet stately of stance and distinguished of feature. The resemblance between the two was, indeed, more one of aura and mannerism than one of specific physical traits. The father's face was fuller, and more ruddy than tanned. His eyes were narrow, his lips somewhat broad. He looked like a man who had enjoyed the fullness of life, but now chose, for some reason which escaped Daran, to live in seclusion.

"Andrew!" The older man greeted his son, the gravel edge of his voice covering the pleasure that his eyes registered when they took in first his son, then the young and extremely attractive woman by his side. "This *is* a surprise!" Whether the surprise was the appearance of Drew himself or his being accompanied by a woman, Daran couldn't tell. As Drew made the introductions, she extended her arm to meet the proferred one.

"Governor Charles, how do you do?"

"Just fine, young woman. And what brings you up here with my very busy son so early this morning?" Was that a note of resignation? she wondered.

Drew came to the rescue. "We've come for breakfast, Dad. That is, if you don't mind." The subtly teasing note was met by a scowl of good-natured rebuke as the man stepped forward from the shadow of the doorway into the bright morning sun. Only then did the golden cast of his predominantly white shock of hair give Daran a flashback to earlier years, when his coloring must have been much as Drew's was now.

As one still-strong arm of the older man settled across her shoulders and the other fell across those of his son, the force of the politician expressed itself fully. To Daran's trained eye, he epitomized the back-slapping, baby-kissing, hand-shaking master who had, in his day, had his fill of all three, yet now, in retirement, could not totally shake the urge. Firmly he drew them into his home.

As rustic as was its appearance, its warmth was undeniable. The throngs of faces, celebrated and unknown alike, were in attendance here, hung for eternity on each and every wall. The furniture was worn, as was its owner, yet bore the same richness, the same stamp of high quality as that one who now led the way toward the small, compactly appointed kitchen, where bacon and eggs were on to fry before Daran could even offer to help.

Drew's relaxation seemed genuine, observed through the intermittent surreptitious glances she cast his way during breakfast. For the most part, the two men exchanged news in what amounted to a sharing of high-level governmental gossip. The father was deeply interested in his son's pet projects. Both men deftly included Daran in the discussion whenever possible and particularly when the issue of the Rights of Minors Act arose. From her standpoint, the interchange between the two was easy and free of the tension to which Drew had referred earlier. Daran found that her own excitement nearly matched that of both men, when Drew outlined the major bills with which the Senate would be dealing before the end of the session. It was a new experience for her to be included in such discussions; Bill had always been more secretive when it came to "men's talk," the real meat of the matter.

The first hint of strain came suddenly, the outcropping of a seemingly innocent—to her ears—statement by the former governor. "You know, Andrew," he began slowly, using the full name which no one else seemed to use as often, "I had a call from the people at GCDC last week." Drew's jaw tightened instantly, yet he listened as his father went on. "They are very concerned about whether Washington is going to come through for them." His eyes studied those of his son expectantly.

"Washington?" the latter prodded skeptically.

"Actually they're counting on the junior senator from their own state." It seemed almost an order; Daran's attention snapped to the face of the older man in surprise, then flew to Drew's in time to witness the chilling of his gray eyes as he spoke tautly.

"They shouldn't."

"Andrew, I've known Fredrick Bornwicke and his crowd for years. Is it so difficult for you, once in a while, to look to your constituency for guidance?"

Drew's lips thinned. "I do look to my constituency whenever possible. In fact, I'm doing it on this issue."

"That's not what GCDC claims," the older man retorted, his own voice growing harder with the continuation of the obvious disagreement. Daran could only sit and listen, totally ignorant of the issue they discussed. Drew's next statement remedied that situation.

"For one thing, Dad, the Greater Connecticut Development Corporation is not the major constituency here. The people of Connecticut are. I was elected to represent them by a majority of them. And that's precisely what I'm trying to do. In the second place, the building code which the Greater Connecticut Development Corporation—" he repeated the full name for emphasis, a habit she would

103

later come to recognize as an often-used and effective one "—has submitted is obscene. Have you any idea of the number of downtown residents who would be displaced and left with no homes if this building goes ahead? Urban renewal is one thing; dispossession is another. With the inflationary spiral as paralyzing as it for those poor people now, the money which GCDC proposes to offer them will take them nowhere." As he spoke, his voice grew more forceful. Instinctively Daran knew that his power was both inborn and well-defined. Now, though his tone lowered, the force remained. "And to think that GCDC has asked for federal funding!" Scornfully he looked away.

"I told Fred that I'd do whatever I could . . ." His father persisted, making his plea an almost personal one. It was this that seemed to aggravate Drew all the more.

"Well, you have, and that's the end of it," he growled.

"Not quite." The governor was far from finished. "There's still that matter of the money that Fred and GCDC contribute every year to your campaign chest . . ."

By this time Daran's stomach was strangely queasy; desperately, she wished that the bacon and eggs she had devoured had been a single slice of dry toast instead. In the instant, she fully understood Drew's hesitancy about spending the night under the same roof as his father. If this was a fair sample of their arguments, a deadlock was inevitable.

When Drew's fist slammed down onto the heavy oak table, she jumped. "I don't really give a damn about Fred Bornwicke and his corporation. And as far as what he can do with his money—" The blunt cut-off of his thought was in belated response to Daran's recoil. A harsh gray gaze took in her pale face, then returned to the stubborn one of his father. "I'd like to show Daran the lake. If you'll excuse us for a minute . . ." The older man seemed as pleased to be rid of his son at that moment as Drew was to have the excuse of an exit. His firm grip on Daran's elbow drew her out the back door, down a narrow earth-covered path, and onto the moistly sandy shore of the private lake. Once there, he dropped her arm, seeming to withdraw into himself in the wake of the disagreement she had witnessed. The calming effect of the scene was well appreciated. As the gentle swell of the water lapped against the shore in soft syncopation, the spring breeze whispered through the branches high above. Slowly she relaxed, as did the tall figure at her side.

"I'm sorry you had to hear that . . . difference of opinion." Evenness had returned to his voice as to the straight line of his lips.

Her response was spontaneous. "Why should you be sorry, Drew?" An unfathomable instinct to comfort sparked her thoughts into words. "I found the first part of the discussion to be fascinating. It was a privilege to have been included in it. As for the last, it's not much different from the conversations I have—or *try* to have—each week with my own mother. Anyway—" she grinned "—it certainly justified your having spent the night at my house, rather than here."

The light note fell flat before his sober cast. "It's very frustrating," he went on, oblivious to her words, "when I try, over and over again, to make a point. I based my campaign on the merits of my past record and my own character. I've tried never to make promises I knew I'd be unable to keep. And I've succeeded. Yet there is always this demand from one contributor or another . . ." With a sigh of resignation, his eyes fell from their study of the opposite shore to that of the upturned face beside him. "What do *you* think, Daran? Where should my loyalties lie?"

Simultaneously stunned by the question yet pleased that

it had been asked, it took her a moment to gather her thoughts. "As a constituent, I would want my interests to be served by the person who supposedly represents me in Washington. As a contributor to a political campaign, I would want to see elected that person whose ideas I most respect. As a citizen of this country, though, I would hope and expect that each senator should ideally be allowed, once elected, to act out of reason and . . . conscience."

As her pulse raced beneath the intensity of the gaze that pierced her being and shot to her soul, she wondered whether he would laugh at her idealism. But the smile that finally curved into a bright, white offering held no ridicule.

"With that kind of eloquence, *you* should be the one in Washington." He spoke softly. "When will you be coming?"

How he had managed to shift the subject as abruptly to this one, which she had no desire to hash out again, she didn't know. Now a dull edge was about all she could put on her response.

"I'm not." Tearing her eyes from his in anticipation of the hypnotic effect he was sure to exert within minutes, she turned her attention to a pair of ducks that swam into view from the marshy area around the bend of the shore.

"Daran, I need you there." His tactic was a new and powerful one. "I feel as strongly about the need for this legislation as you do. You are one of the leaders in the field, at this point. I know that we have our differences regarding the specifics, but that can be worked out, I'm sure." Dumbfounded at the straight-talking, conciliatory effect of his words, she could only watch as he turned to stare out across the water, his mind miles farther away to the south. "You have to understand politics. Above everything else, it is the art of compromise. I am trying to formulate legislation which will be as strong as possible and still have a chance for passage. The opposition is staunch in some quarters." He was silent for a while, pondering the job that awaited him when he returned to the nation's hub later that very morning. Then, as though recalling her presence once more, he blinked as he addressed her personally again.

"I could use your support."

With a deftness she was later to marvel at, he had taken the offensive skillfully, turning the difference between them into something both positive and powerful. The turmoil of the dilemma whirled about in her brain. For long moments she looked at the sincerity of his features, the character portrayed therein, the dedication of which his earlier words had hinted.

"I . . . really don't want to go . . . to Washington." She hedged feebly.

"What have you got against Washington?" he asked, puzzled for not the first time. Squirming under his close scrutiny, she finally chose to ignore his question.

"Wouldn't it be possible for me to make some kind of contribution right here from Hartford?" It was no longer a question of whether she would work with Drew, though she was totally unaware of having consciously made that decision. Rather, the issue now was where the two would collaborate.

"That would be difficult, Daran." He stood not two feet from her, speaking directly and honestly. "As it is—" a raised brow glittered beneath the sun which, in turn, sparkled off the water "—my office has had one hell of a time squeezing some basic information out of you." The gently accusatory glance he sent her hit its mark; suddenly she felt guilty at having ignored so blatantly the requests of one Stanley Morrow.

"I apologize for that," she offered softly, hoping to suggest that she would be more helpful in the future. But

107

Drew's mind had not strayed far from the track. Now his words grew more urgent.

"Summer will be here soon. The bulk of the hearings will be held during that time. Surely you could spare some time—if you were truly interested in the cause."

His implication was obvious, as was the inevitability of her protest. "Of course I'm interested!" she bit back. "You know that! If it hadn't been for my interest, I would never have put myself in the position of having to deal with the political establishment in *any* form." The flashing of gold in her eyes gave added impetus to the thought that possessed her. It was the same cynicism back to haunt her again.

"Then come to Washington!" he urged her once more, deliberately bypassing that note of bitterness to move onward.

"I can't. . . ."

Instinctively he felt that there was a very personal reason behind her refusal. He was also acutely aware of the hint of fear that hovered in her vision. Another tack entirely seemed in order.

"It's your responsibility, Daran. You've been very vocal for the past few weeks. Here's your chance to put your money where your mouth is, so to speak. Or is it all a bluff—an ego-driven bluff?"

"No!" Furious now, she snapped back at him with every ounce of her determination. "It's no bluff. Your bill is diluted. It needs . . . something . . ."

His own response, coming in a low, rich croon, was no less insistent. "It needs *you.* If you want to change things, you'd better get off that pretty little butt of yours and *do it.* Either that, or keep your mouth shut."

As it happened, she did both. Turning in a huff, she stomped her way back to the cabin for a brief farewell to the governor, then, still without a word to Drew, ensconced herself in his car for the drive back to her house. The occasional speculative glances he sent her way were never seen, so blinded was she with her own plight. She even missed the smugness of the smile that gradually found its way to his well-formed lips as she transferred to her own car at the house and preceded out the driveway and onto the main road. It was only when she looked behind through her rearview mirror and found that he had turned off the highway, that she realized she had never said good-bye.

CHAPTER 5

Washington was beautiful at the start of June, all green and rich and warm, very warm. Tree-lined streets struck their lush-boughed canopy over the comings and goings of the city, its cultured verdance accented with an abundance of color, from the purple lilacs and the white azaleas, to the more vibrant red roses, pink tulips, and golden daffodils. The bumblebees winged from bud to bud, much as did the governmental players scooting from place to place as the pace of the Congressional session began to pick up.

From the cool comfort of her perch, high in the air-conditioned suite that had been graciously provided for her, Daran watched it all. Her admiring eye touched on granite-corded avenues, their structures scrubbed and fresh and proud. Her mind shared that pride in this, her nation's capital. Had she been a visitor from a foreign land, she could have been no more impressed. As a child she had been to the city several times. Yet now, through the gaze of the adult she had become, it held much more.

Recollection of the past few weeks—and how she had finally come to be here—slowly filtered back to her. She hadn't seen Drew since the morning they had breakfasted with his father, then had quarreled themselves later. There had never been a formal acknowledgment that she would accede to his request to come to Washington. Yet, when the calls began to come in from the senator's aides, and particularly and with regularity from John Hollings regarding the specifics of her stay, she silently acquiesced. Actually the arrangements that had been worked out were ideal. For the major parts of June and July, August if necessary, she would spend Tuesdays through Thursdays in Washington, working with Drew and his aides on formulation of the Rights of Minors Act. All other work in which she was involved—her patients, her writing, and, most importantly, the Child Advocacy Project—had been scheduled for time on Mondays, Fridays, and Saturdays, when she would be in Connecticut. Somewhere in between would be sandwiched the leisure to work in her garden, to sun, to explore the state which she had never seen in summer before.

Turning, her fancy caught on the small but exquisite arrangement of cut flowers that had been delivered soon after her arrival. "Welcome to my world. A.S.C." the note had read, very simply, very thoughtfully. Now she wondered exactly how she had come to be in his world. Originally her decision had been based on the argument he had made so potently to her that day by the shore of the lake. It was her civic responsibility. Given the opportunity and the strength of her feelings for her Child Advocacy Project and Drew's own Rights of Minors Act, she could not have refused.

But there was more to it than that. After long hours of self-examination, Daran realized how deeply she had been affected by the discussion between father and son on that same, fateful day. The excitement was hard to forget. To be included in it as an active participant was something she could never have passed up. In the end, however, there was one major determinant in her change of mind.

Drew. Even barring deep analysis of her feelings toward the man, she found herself drawn by the charisma which drew so many others to his side. An enigma to her in many ways, he succeeded in fascinating her to the exclusion of all the notions that had preceded him. There was the same wariness of the process and its major actors, the Congress and its laws, which had possessed her since the days she had been so torn apart by Bill Longley, and there was always the possibility that the fates would, at some point, conspire to throw her into the same room as that man who was once her husband. Yet the aura of power which Drew Charles exuded, the implicit cloak of immunity which had accompanied his personal interest in her, was enough for her, for the time being at least, to ignore the other. Though she could not yet explain it herself, she found herself looking forward to working with Drew.

A resigned smile curved her lips at the thought of how well Drew had handled her. From the start he had sensed her resistance to him, his image, and his government establishment. The breakthrough had been on a personal level, allowing her glimpses—all impressive—of the man himself, before subjecting her to the senator in action. Now she was finally to see the latter—and her feelings were mixed.

The soft ring of the phone jarred her concentration. She walked the short distance to the small glass coffee table and answered the phone. The voice at the other end was the now familiar one of John Hollings, checking to make sure that the accommodations were satisfactory, forewarning her that one of the other legislative aides, a young woman named Laura Speranzo, would be up with a folder of the latest information on the Rights of Minors Act, and, finally, announcing that Drew would himself be by to see her sometime around seven.

Replacing the receiver, she glanced at her watch. Barely five o'clock—what was she to do with herself for the next two hours? And precisely what did he want to see her about? Her instructions had been explicit; she was expected at his office the following morning. What now?

There was no time to ponder as the light knock at the door of her suite diverted her attention. It was, on the button, the aide whom John had mentioned. An attractive woman of no more than twenty-six years, she introduced herself as the senator's assistant on matters regarding the Judiciary Committee, of which he was a member, and, more specifically, the Civil Liberties Subcommittee, of which he was the chairman, and before which the Rights of Minors Act was to have its preliminary hearing. After depositing several piles of folders and miscellaneous papers on the coffee table, the young woman excused herself with a promise of seeing her in the morning, then left. For the first time, Daran speculated on those others with whom she would be working. Up until now, her role had been in a vacuum. Tomorrow would change that.

The time flew by as she slowly plodded through the material that the aide had delivered. There was background research on attempts at such a bill and its failure in the past. There were analyses as to the causes of those failures, then state-by-state analyses of the positions of the various senators on the bill as proposed by Drew. There were memoranda and amendments, pros and cons on each issue touched on in the bill, included among which was the detailed paper she had submitted shortly after she had seen Drew that last time. Even that had been exciting to her, far from the drudgery she might have imagined. For not only did she have the opportunity to state her own views, but then there was the chance to rebut them herself. It had been an informative exercise, raising more than one question in her mind concerning those positions which she had, hitherto, postulated.

The immersion in these printed materials served to take her mind from the impending meeting with Drew. For, despite the reasons she had previously given herself for finally agreeing to come to Washington, there was one which she had steadfastly chosen to ignore. Now, however, such treatment was impossible. An anticipatory tingle ran down her spine as a sound in the hall passed her door, then moved on.

Drew Charles was a phenomenally attractive man. Like it or not, he excited her physically, as he did in those other ways she had already acknowledged. He made her feel like a woman, something she had fought against for the past five years but which now a distinct part of her craved. But Washington was full of attractive and available women. Hadn't the young woman who had stopped by earlier been a prime example? Laura Speranzo was a legislative aide of Drew's; did he see her off-hours as well? Brushing aside the thought as both irrelevant and inappropriate, she looked at her watch. Seven-thirty, already! Her own absorption had failed to note his tardiness.

In a moment's return to the past, tardiness seemed the norm. Bill had kept her waiting, time and again, when some other political appointment had been more important than the time and patience of the wife who waited at home. Bitterness surged through her in hindsight, some of it lingering to tinge the fresh outlook of the present. When a strong pair of knuckles finally hit the door at a quarter past eight, her mood was taut. Geared for a fight, unjustifiable as it would have been, she opened the door. Amazement replaced her testiness in the instant. Only later would she realize that he had pulled it on her again, changing the subject, as it were, when she was prepared to let him have a piece of her mind. Now she stood mute as her widened amber eyes took in the vision before her.

Where she had expected the stately and composed senator from Connecticut, neat, cool, and handsome, she found a very handsome man who looked as if he had just lost a race with time. Tie loosened, top button of his shirt undone, hair casually askew, jacket thrown carelessly over his arm, his panting and sweating suggested some major exertion in transit to her door. And his eyes—his eyes were full of a fury that held her speechless. It was in this state that she watched him stalk into the room, head directly for the bar at its far side, and fix himself a light drink.

"Damn it! We were supposed to adjourn at six; I had Wright's word on that. *Two more hours* they ran, just so Higgins and Axelrod could trade barbs. If it hadn't been for my own interest in that fool trade reinvestment program, I would have gotten up and left, like so many of my colleagues did. If it weren't for the tobacco industry at home . . ." His voice trailed off as he looked directly at Daran, whose back was flush against the closed door of the suite. "I'm sorry, Daran. I had no intention of keeping you waiting." Obviously he had run most of the way from the Senate floor to her hotel, a distance of quite a few city blocks.

"Don't worry about it." She smiled softly, all irritation she had felt moments earlier spending itself. "I've had plenty to keep me busy." A slender hand gestured toward the papers strewn on the table. "One of your aides dropped them off a little while ago." Her subconscious banter had been intended to provide him those few extra moments to relax. He took even longer, staring at her as the ice in his tumbler melted beneath the warmth of the large hand that surrounded it. Finally he smiled widely, a sign of sure recovery.

"How have you been?" The rich melody of his voice caressed her as did the eyes that now skimmed the light-weight cotton wraparound dress she wore, the lengths of her tanned legs, the slim-strapped high-heeled open-toed sandals, returning at long last to her face, flushed now, as though she had run the distance herself.

"I'm fine." The softness of her voice belied the inexplicable excitement she felt.

"You're looking . . . well."

"So are you."

A hearty laugh burst through the firmness of his lips. "That's a joke. I've never felt more grungy in my life. I had every intention of getting home to shower and shave before showing up here." The twinkle that warmed his gray-eyes gaze spurred her on; it was Drew Charles's own form of hypnosis at its most powerful tonight.

"I'm glad you came directly."

He smiled more gently as he continued to mesmerize her. "So am I. But I'm afraid it means that dinner will have to wait a little longer."

Dinner, she had not expected. This was to have been a business meeting, a preview of what she could expect the following day. Now, as her brows knit in bemusement, Drew's own lowered in suspicion. "You mean to say that John did not mention that?" She shook her head no and that sent him quickly on. "You haven't eaten, have you?" Again she shook her head. "Good. Let's go."

As she wondered whether she was actually getting used to this man's spontaneity, she crossed the room to pick up her handbag and the room key, then passed through the door before Drew. In the instant came the realization that this was one of the very things that drew her to him. He was, in a most pleasant way, totally unpredictable. And, having grown up with a breed of politician who possessed a one-track mind, it was a refreshing change.

"You're unusually quiet tonight," he murmured, ushering her into the elevator, pressing the lobby button, then turning to face her.

Smiling, she shrugged. "You seem to be handling the

conversation just fine on your own." Her teasing note was well accepted.

Once again, though, he took her off-guard. "You don't mind a walk, do you?"

"Hmm?" she mumbled, confused.

"If you don't mind, we can walk to my place. It's not far—a ten-, fifteen-minute walk at most. I do want to clean up some."

"No, the walk is fine. It's a lovely night." Indeed it was, yet that fact did not help pacify the rumbling in her stomach at the thought of going to Drew's place. Was it a line, one of the oldies but goodies? Would he make his move there?

Since that night in her house, the memory of his control, over both her and himself, had nagged at her. Even now she wasn't quite sure what she wanted. His company was so very pleasing to her, as was the character that had slowly unfolded for her, that she was hesitant to spoil the foundation of their relationship with something she couldn't quite handle yet. But could she ever handle it? Did she want to?

"Oh, Lord, here we go again!" he exclaimed, raising his eyes to the ceiling as Daran's flashed toward him in puzzlement. "The war," he explained in a conspiratorial whisper as the door of the elevator opened and he escorted her quickly, with the diligence of a man who does not want to be stopped by either someone he knows or someone he does not, into the lobby, then out to the street. It was only when they had put a block between themselves and the more populated hotel area that he stopped and turned her to face him, strong arms on her shoulders brooking no resistance.

"Listen, Daran," he began, serious yet gentle. "I told you once before that I have no intention of hurting you. That is a promise."

117

The amber eyes that looked up at him held a note of the cynicism he had sampled on other occasions. "Politicians are expert at making promises. Somehow, when it comes to keeping them, there is always a more important issue."

"Not here. Not now." The vehemence in his tone gave emphasis to words she did not dare refute. For several seconds he studied her pained expression, then turned, took her hand in the most innocent of gestures, and pulled her beside him to walk onward. "You know, I have this strange feeling that you will be the greatest test I may ever have to face. I keep telling myself that it is your mind I want . . . yet my hands keep itching to . . ." The sidelong glance he threw down at her said the rest. "Ach, forget it!" he murmured beneath his breath. At that very moment Daran knew that she would never be able to follow that particular order.

Drew's apartment, it turned out, was more like a twenty-minute walk. Daran didn't mind a bit. Not only did the added minutes further delay the intimacy that their destination, regardless of Drew's pledge, had to suggest, but it gave her an opportunity to see one part of the city, at least, first-hand and close up. The senator proved to be a skilled tour guide, pointing out the specific embassies they passed, identifying other buildings that lined the blocks they walked, even explaining the overall scheme of the layout of the city.

When an elegant brown-marbled apartment building loomed before them and he drew her past its starched security guard, Daran knew that they had reached his home. Six floors later, a broad expanse of living area opened itself to her close inspection as Drew excused himself to shower and change. The condominium—he had indicated his ownership on the way up—was exquisitely decorated, simple yet finely appointed, much of the decorative effect achieved by a collection of souvenirs—

sculpture, artwork, even furniture—from foreign lands. Later Drew was to explain where he had bought each, elaborating with great color on the nature and experience of each trip. Daran had traveled her share, yet in no way could her own experiences rival his for sheer intensity of purpose, if nothing else. The pleasure he felt on the road, at seeing new places, confronting different civilizations, was obvious. Daran could do nothing but admire it.

"Ah, you've made yourself at home, I see." Several long strides brought Daran from the hallway to the sofa on which she sat, deeply engrossed in a photo album whose gold-embossed title, *CHINA*, had simply been too much of a temptation. "That was from my trip three years ago. There have been regular Congressional delegations to Peking since diplomatic relations were resumed. I was fortunate to be included with one of those earlier groups."

"Who took these photographs?" Even to her untrained eye, they were technically perfect, totally aside from the subject matter. Had there been an official photographer along on the trip, making this album but one more of the perquisites of Drew's position?

"I did." As though to skim over that bit of enlightenment, he suddenly leaned forward from his perch on the arm of the sofa, his own arms straddling her body as he pointed out one thing or another; small points but significant and very interesting—had she only been able to concentrate. His pose ruled out that possibility. Too aware was she of the hair-roughened texture of the forearms that sided hers, the warmth that spread from his chest to her back, his clean and fresh scent, and his breath against her hair. This first challenge of the evening was in keeping her eyes on the prints rather on the strong hands that hovered beside and over them. The second was in fighting the urge to lean just that slight bit back against his strength. When he finally paused in his discourse, she made the mistake of looking up at his face. His sandy hair was darker than usual beneath the lingering dampness of his shower; he was fresh shaven and breathtaking.

"Am I boring you?" he asked slyly, returning the eyeful with one of his own, the hint of mischief darting about the edges of his mouth.

A soft flush crept up her cheeks as she realized she had been staring. "Of course not. It's fascinating." Tearing her eyes from the true crux of her fascination, she turned the next page. Mercifully Drew did not force the issue, though neither did he move farther from her. Well aware of her state as well as of his own, he continued his narrative.

The next half hour was spent in much this way. Having never been to China, nor seen an inside view such as this album offered, Daran was entranced. Drew, too, relived the trip with her; his enthusiasm was contagious. When the leather binding closed at last, he straightened. The note of hesitancy in his voice when he finally spoke brought her head around quickly.

"Look, Daran, I wonder . . ." A side glance at his watch gave him a moment's respite. "I hope you won't take this the wrong way. I assure you, my intentions are honorable." Both his hands lifted, open-palmed, indicative that he hid nothing. "Would you mind terribly if we had some supper here? I mean, there are any number of fine restaurants we could go to—and I feel guilty not showing you the town on your first night here—but, well, the days are so hectic that I do prefer a nice, quiet evening. How about it?" His eyes melted into her as he cocked his head in a boyish way. "I'm not bad in the kitchen. With your help, we could manage to put something together."

"That sounds great!" she heard herself say, accompanied, no less, by a smile which matched his in its even whiteness. Not for a minute did she stop to recall her hesitancy in coming to this, his home, in the first place.

Rather, she had just spent a most pleasant few minutes here and wished for nothing more than that it continue. Though the clock neared ten, she was not tired.

"Are you sure you don't mind not going out?"

"Yes, I'm sure." The soft smile persisted as he looked at her; she was under his spell once more. Despite his good intentions, he was as helplessly drawn to the lips that stood, barely parted, in silent invitation. His kiss was soft and gentle, sweet and soulful. Daran could have totally succumbed to its power had not Drew himself pulled back. An oath fell against the dark waves at the crown of her head, where his lips took refuge.

"Damn it, Daran. Why do you do that? How do you expect me to stay away from you when you look at me like that?" His arms had encircled her back, drawing her head against his chest. The loud thunder against her ear was his heartbeat, as erratic as hers at that moment. Shame filled her as she knew he was right. It had, after all, been *her* desire that he not make love to her. To be a tease was unfair.

"I'm sorry. I didn't realize I was doing anything . . ." It was, indeed, the truth, though whether he would believe her was doubtful. Yet there was no way that she could confess the hold he had over her. The only comfort the situation afforded was in the knowledge that she did herself wield a certain power, to which his ragged breathing now attested.

For a long moment of would-be punishment, his arms tightened around her, squeezing mercilessly. Then, with a groan, he released her. "Well, don't let it happen again." Another order she would be unable to obey, she mused with resignation. Then, abruptly, her hand was clasped and she was drawn from her seat. "Let's get a move on. I'm hungry." There was no double meaning intended in his declaration. That the man was famished became evident twenty minutes later, when the two sat down to an informal dinner of steak, salad, and Chablis.

"I enjoyed meeting your father," she began, relaxing back to watch her companion refill their glasses with wine. "Have you seen him since?"

"No. I haven't been home since. But that will be rectified soon."

"Oh?" Was he trying to tell her something?

"The summer season is an active one in the state. There are country fairs, crafts shows, outdoor everything from one town to the next. Stan has filled two weekends a month for me." The speculative gaze he showered on her gave her but a moment's warning of the impending invitation. "Perhaps you'd like to see some of it with me?"

There was no denying her excitement at the prospect. "I've never spent the summer in Connecticut. I'd love to see those things you've mentioned."

"You may have second thoughts once you discover the pace with which we have to race from one to another." A tawny eyebrow arched in fair warning.

"I can keep up. I've had plenty of practice." The words had slipped out without her realizing their implication. The mistake was made; she steeled herself for the inevitable follow-up.

"And where did you get that practice?" The sharpness of the gray-eyed gaze belied the gentleness of his tone.

"Oh, at home, when I was growing up." Her attempt at minimizing the slip was thwarted instantly.

"Was your family involved with politics?"

"Only indirectly. But surely you know that. Didn't you check up on me before you drafted me?"

To her deep surprise, he shook his head. "There was no FBI rundown, on you, Daran." His sarcasm hung in the air, then faded, fallen victim to his curiosity. "I've never come across a Patterson from the Midwest. But then—"

122

he corrected himself quickly "—you told me that your father had died. Was it your stepfather who was involved?"

The last thing Daran wanted was for him to learn more about her than he knew at that moment. It took every bit of wiliness for her to detour the discussion with some minor semblance of nonchalance. "Yes, it was. In many ways he reminds me of your father. He must be lonesome, living alone by the lake out there, even though it is so very beautiful. Does he get out much?"

The even stare that pierced her with its sharp gray shaft left no doubt that he saw through her ploy. Why he let it pass, she was not sure. On that score, she would ask no questions.

"He has many friends. And, yes, he does see them from time to time. But he chooses to live alone and he seems relatively . . . satisfied."

It seemed a strange word—satisfied—to describe the situation. Happy, perhaps. Peaceful, perhaps. Content, perhaps. But satisfied? "When did your mother die?"

A frown brought Drew's brows together as he looked down at the empty plate before him. "She's been gone a long time now—fourteen, fifteen years, at least."

"Were you close?"

"Yes . . . and no." Daran held her breath, waiting for him to elaborate. After what seemed an interminable silence, he did. "She and I were very much alike. It was just the two of us as I grew up. My father was simply never there." The hardening of his voice spoke of his lasting resentment. "But, with a man as forceful as my father, it was inevitable, despite all of my mother's protests, that I should become involved. She died before it actually came to be, but the anticipation, the grooming for a political career, the endless times I had to tag along after my father —that got to her. I was torn—that got to her too."

"How did she die?" Thoroughly involved in the psychological drama being sketchily recreated for her, Daran's question was a spontaneous one. The answer came so quietly, with its blend of guilt and sorrow, that she had to strain to hear it.

"She died as she lived—alone. They say it was a stroke. I know it was loneliness, boredom, the lack of the will to live." The accuracy of his conclusion was not for Daran to judge. That Drew blamed himself, in some part, for the fate of his mother was obvious. Its further ramification, however, would not have been imagined had it not been for the force of the sudden outburst that followed. His voice remained low, though his words were spoken through tightly clenched jaws. "I could not ask any woman to live the life I do. Not after that . . ."

The ensuing silence gave Daran a chance to recover from his bitter vow. He had, in his words, reinforced her own feelings on the matter. Life with Bill—married to a political beast—had been cruel torture from the start. Or had it been Bill who was the beast? For the first time she had to face that possibility. But why now? It only took the time to sip the last of her wine for Daran to come up with an answer. It was Drew. Drew was as different from Bill as night from day. In the short time she had spent with Drew, she had rarely thought of him as the politician she knew, for a fact, he was. When she was with him, thought of that all-consuming machine of government was nonexistent aside from the specific discussions that revolved around it and that had so comfortably drawn her into its web in an inoffensive way. That was the difference. Drew Charles was not only a politician. He was, as he had so insistently pointed out to her on one very vocal occasion, a man as well. Whereas other men might be swallowed up by the machine, Drew would merely laugh in its face and

124

turn his back on it if that seemed the only course for survival. He was a survivor above all else.

Yet his thoughts lingered on one who had not survived. It was as if, having opened the floodgates, the flow could not be stopped. His voice was low and smooth, its edge of steel barely sheathed. "I see women every day, wives, even girl friends of various of my colleagues, who suffer as my mother did. There was nothing unique about her. It's a disease. The political bug is a hard one to shake. It becomes one's mistress, spoiling all other relationships." As he seethed on in his quietly forceful manner, Daran's own prejudices clamored to agree. "The crime against children in the political arena is terrible. Here we are, trying to guarantee children certain basic rights, when all we have to do is to look around us to see a generation being neglected pitifully."

Daran had never seen Drew so agitated. As he spoke, her own level of agitation had risen as she had relived her own past. Though they had never made it as a couple to Washington, she and Bill had suffered that disease to which Drew referred first-hand. The matter of children was particularly poignant; Daran had wanted them desperately when first they contemplated marriage. Mercifully she had not conceived.

When Drew looked her straight in the eye and repeated his vow, "I would never ask a woman to sacrifice her life for me," she was stunned. Yet her own suffering was too fresh in her mind to disagree.

"You shouldn't. It would be very cruel." Her thoughts were on Bill, that *he* should have been the one making the vow now. Only when Drew seemed to snap from his own anger to send her a puzzled glance did she realize how far her emotions had strayed. Eager to make amends, she smiled as warmly as possible. "I'm sorry. I was thinking of something else. That sounded terrible."

125

A pulse in his temple throbbed visibly. "You have every right to believe what you want."

"But that's not what I believe—that is, I'm not sure . . ." In fact, she was not. For years now, her being had been hardened to men in general, and this political maelstrom in particular. Now she *was* not quite sure.

After what seemed an eternal pause, Drew grinned. "When Dr. Daran Patterson isn't sure about something, it must mean that she has either had too much wine or that she is exhausted. In either case, I'd better drive you home."

Fearful of protesting, lest he push her to discuss her quandary, she accompanied him without argument, this time in his car, a sober navy sedan which was a far cry from the sporty silver one he kept in Connecticut.

"Laura Speranzo will be by to pick you up at seven-thirty tomorrow morning. Once a month I get all my aides together for a breakfast. You happened to arrive at the right time." A bright grin flashed her way as one hand left the wheel to squeeze hers, which lay idly in her lap. His touch was enough to reawaken any senses that might have succumbed to the wine. "Senator Brande, from New Mexico, will be speaking. And you'll have a chance to meet all the others in the office." Nodding, Daran accepted the fact that he would not be picking her up himself. Why she had hoped it, she was reluctant to say. Reading her thoughts, he said as he pulled the car up just across the street from her hotel, "I'd give you a lift myself if it weren't for the petty jealousies it might cause." He was teasing at first, then he sobered enough to convey the truth of his message. "It's a very delicate thing—balancing the egos of one's staff. And a staff is critical to the success and power of any senator. You'll see that for yourself." Once more she had to admire him for the sensitivity that his words suggested.

126

Silently she reached for the door to let herself out. Never one to sit on ceremony, it had seemed perfectly natural. When Drew's long torso stretched across to still her departure, she looked back in surprise. "Can you get up to your room all right?" One hand was on the back of the seat by her head, the other covering hers on the door handle. His face was mere inches from hers, its nearness sending shock waves through her which had nothing to do with the suddenness of his move.

"I think so." Then she teased back in a frail attempt at diluting the sensuous havoc he caused. "After all, we wouldn't want to give fuel for gossip." Had he not mentioned but moments before the existence of jealousies among the in-group, the quip would never have surfaced. It was taken, mercifully, in the good humor in which it had been offered.

"To hell with gossip," he growled playfully. "If I see you to your room, I won't leave. You know how much I want you . . ." The last was uttered with a depth of desire which, in truth, had been building all evening. Even in spite of the negativity of the discussion at his home earlier, the fact of the chemical attraction between the two was undeniable. At that moment Daran would mindlessly have invited him to walk her in, drugged as she was by his nearness.

His body was all male, sending a telltale tingle through her. Remembrance of the touch of his lips on hers deepened that tingle to a shudder he could not have missed, bent intimately around her as he was. When the hand behind curved about her neck and he straightened, drawing her toward him, she went willingly. Earlier his kiss had been one of reacquaintance; now there was pure hunger in it.

The dark of night held from her all things visual. Sensa-

127

tion reigned supreme. Receiving and returning his embrace in kind, she dove happily into the sea of his passion, wishing nothing more than to drown there. Yet he held her afloat, teasing her with a new twist of his lips or a deeper forage of his tongue. His hand caressed her shoulder, then fell to mold gently the full curve of her breast.

"Drew, please . . ." she began breathlessly when he finally released her lips. A large forefinger instantly straightened against them to still her words, be they invitation or protest. For some reason he did not wish to know. Rather, firmly pulling himself away from her, he cleared his throat.

"You'd better go on up, Daran. We've got an early morning tomorrow." It seemed, indeed, a repetition of the past; once more, politics had made its grand intrusion on her life. This time, however, it may have been a godsend.

"Drew—" she began again, her purpose a mystery even to herself, only knowing that she did not want the evening to end on that last jarring note. Again he silenced her.

"Shh. Let me be noble . . . just for tonight." For a brief moment his head turned her way. Even in the flickering beam of a passing headlight the strain on his face was evident. Perhaps he was right; enough had been said and done for one evening.

Sliding back over the seat, she let herself out, ran across the street, and disappeared into the hotel lobby without a backward glance, intent only on seeking the solace of her room and its privacy to ponder her feelings.

But those feelings were far from simple, as was the man who sparked them. If only he were the typical political devil she had envisioned that very first day in her office at Trinity. Negative as her dealings with him might have been, he would at least have been predictable. And resistible. Drew Charles was *neither.* And there was yet another side of the man to be seen, one to which she would be introduced the following morning. It was her perverse prayer that he would prove to be every bit as offensive a senator-in-action as the very worst of the lot. Somehow, however, she doubted that that would be the case.

CHAPTER 6

The next few days left Daran little time to ponder the depths of her own feelings. Whereas as at home in Connecticut she was, by virtue of the professional roles in which she found herself, an organizer, an adviser, a leader, here in Washington she was one of the group. If she had expected that less executive status to be a more passive one, however, she was mistaken. From the start, the life of the governmental servant took her by storm, both intellectually and physically. Not only were there a myriad of varying issues to be considered at any given time, but the rigor of meetings, fact-finding, telephoning, and chasing after one legislator or another would try the energy of even the most conditioned athlete.

It began with the staff breakfast the following morning. The young woman whom she had met so briefly the day before was at her door five minutes ahead of time. Fortunately Daran's own excitement had woken her long before the official call came through. Showered, and dressed in a safari-style shirtwaist dress of lightweight cotton, she labored for long minutes with her hair, fastening it at the nape of her neck both for coolness and for a continuation of the mature image that the simple bone sandals, the gold chain and hoop earrings, and the wide obilike sash imparted. A dash of cologne and a dash of makeup concluded her dallying. When she opened the door for Laura Speranzo,

130

she felt confidence in the properly poised appearance she made.

Of the many surprises in store for her, the first was the overall youth of the workers who comprised the senator's staff. Aside from the major legislative aides, of which there appeared at fast count to be five, the second echelon of assistants were young—most younger than herself—and enthusiastic. The friendly hand of John Hollings, who seemed to manage the others, was at her elbow from the moment she entered the room, guiding her from one to the other, making the introductions with an unmistakable flair, telling her just enough about each one to help her keep them straight. A cup of coffee and a cheese danish mysteriously found their way into her hands. So preoccupied was she in meeting these new people that Drew, for a large part, escaped her attention. Only later, after Senator Brande had given a short talk on the pending defense-spending bill, and the general milling commenced once more, did she note that, as host, he had moved quietly from one guest to another, shunning the spotlight himself, chatting personally with his staff.

As Daran was diverted, she had missed the intermittent glances he cast her way as he made his rounds. When the tall form suddenly materialized by her side, she was—for the first time that morning—strangely unsure of herself. Up to that point self-assurance had come naturally. For all the competitive spirit that had to exist in a group such as this, its members had welcomed her with courtesy and interest. But Drew she already knew, in a fashion; how was she to act toward him?

To her immediate relief, the senator himself established the guideline. "How are you, Daran?" The rhetorical question, overheard both by John Hollings and by Leo Alteris, with whom she had been talking moments before, was rapidly followed up by more very deliberate chatter.

"It was fortunate that you came in yesterday and were able make it this morning. You won't find any better danish in all of Washington." The gleam in his eye touched on both other faces before returning to hers. "I see you've met Leo. John must have told you that he is in charge of matters before the Judiciary Committee. You'll be working primarily with him while you're here." The tone of voice was smooth and even, carrying the same warmth—and no more—that it had to the ears of each of his other staffers. There was a hand on neither her elbow, her waist, nor her shoulder. In his office setting Drew Charles observed all proprieties. Not so, necessarily, his staff.

Before Daran knew what was happening, the man named Leo, who was evidently to be her overseer, stepped closer and did put a casually intimate arm over her slim shoulders. "I owe you my thanks, Senator. Dr. Patterson may be just what we need." The hint of a deeper mischief, written so blatantly in his features, went much further than his words. For the first time Daran took a good look at him. Perhaps in his early thirties, the man was of average height and build and very good looking by all normal standards. Why Daran had not noticed this when she had first met him was no mystery; in this office, those normal standards were sadly relegated to the paper-shredder—for the boss of the office set an entirely new and far higher standard.

It was the senator's voice, a bit stronger now, as though in echo of her thoughts. "Dr. Patterson is here to work, Leo. Keep that in mind. I'll be expecting twice as much work from both of you before those hearings are over." A chill of premonition passed through Daran, not so much inspired by his words as by the sharp eye which, with an awesome visual touch, removed the tentative weight of her coworker's arm from her shoulder. It was obvious that the

132

senator would stand for no mixing of business and pleasure when it came to his office. But then, isn't that what she had known all along? Where politics was the name of the game, romance was ruled out. In Bill's case, politics had been his be-all and end-all; there *was* nothing else. Drew had already proven that he was a human being as well as a politician. Yet his reaction in this particular situation, she was sure, had been intended as a lesson for her. While she worked for him, there would be no fooling around—it was as blunt as that. And, for the time being at least, she could live with that ground rule. For if she was to be working as hard as he suggested, sleepless nights such as the last one would definitely be detrimental.

The gathering lasted no more than an hour, with Drew excusing himself promptly at eight-thirty to attend an informal briefing at the State Department. With the dispersal of the others, Daran found herself closeted with a more sober Leo Alteris and two other research assistants. Assuming either that Drew's warning had made its mark on the other man, or that the weight of the workload beneath which they now struggled had erased any amorous imaginings, she breathed a sigh of relief. It was enough that she did not have to worry about the unwanted advances of an ardent admirer; there was too much to deal with, of a more critical nature, concerning the Rights of Minors Act.

Her hotel room never looked as good as it did that night when, exhausted, she finally returned there. For the greater part of the day she had not left the office, painstakingly explaining then arguing her views before an often skeptical Leo Alteris. It came as some surprise to her to learn that he had himself been responsible for much of the original wording of the bill. That accounted for some of his resistance to change. The rest was due to Drew's occasional joining in the discussion. While the words may have been

133

Leo's, the ideas were irrevocably those of the senator. At long last the multitude of arguments that Daran had prepared before that original meeting in Hartford were of use to her. Staunchly she held her ground, offering specifics and statistics to illustrate why a particular item in the bill would be ineffective or another would be too weak to make a permanent dent in the situation which had been buiding for years.

One source of contention was the juvenile court system. It was this problem that occupied her thoughts that night, then carried over into her attack the following morning when, following a short break to afford a group of Connecticut Boy Scouts a tour of the office, the think tank on the Rights of Minors Act met again.

"But, Leo," she began, laying papers out before the dark head bent at the desk, "it's not enough to state that cases must be brought before a judge within a 'reasonable period of time,'" or even 'three months from the date of the complaint.'" You have no idea what I see out there over and over and over again. A complaint is brought against a juvenile, perhaps a runaway charge brought by a parent, an assault charge brought by an elderly man in a housing development, even a larceny charge brought by a store owner, and a process begins that is nearly endless." Sitting forward in her seat, she pleaded her case vehemently.

"First the determination has to be made that the defendant is a juvenile. Then, if he needs it, court counsel must be appointed. And if you think that the average lawyer who represents the juvenile offender on a court-appointed basis is truly committed to serving the best interests of that child, you're mistaken. I'm not even sure whether, given the mass of red tape to be waded through, *any* lawyer could do better. When the case is finally brought before a judge, it may be heard, held over until the next day or the next week or three months from then. It's a disgrace, what some call justice."

She paused for a breath. Leo's dark eyes held hers, the only concession he made to the arrival of the senator being the passing of several charts and pages of statistics to the lean form that moved silently from the door to the corner of the desk.

"Go on." It was Drew's voice, bearing that same self-control that characterized his comings and goings in the office. For a split second she was taken aback. In the times they had spent together, she and Drew had never gotten as far as the specifics of her fault-finding with his bill. Now he sat before her, resplendent in his navy blue blazer, white shirt, and dark gray pants. Features intent, yet with a definite kindness to them, he awaited the resumption of her discourse. This was why she was here—for the discussions she now held with the man and his aides. The deep breath she took caught for just a minute as the knowing twinkle beamed her way from the warm gray of Drew's gaze. It was the first truly personal gesture he had made since the night they had dined together. It was more in self-defense against what threatened to disconcert her even more that she ventured on.

For the better part of half an hour, Drew sat with them. His questions to Daran were well-timed and pithy, shearing the excess from the discussion as he pondered the core of her arguments. His head was bent, deep in thought, when his personal secretary, Antonia Brown, poked her head into the office to remind him of a hearing he was to attend on the matter of farming subsidies.

Daran's amber eyes followed the lithe form as it disappeared down the hall. "How can he switch from one topic to another like that, at the snap of a finger?"

"They're all like that—or, the good ones, at least," Leo quickly explained. "*I* could never do it; I have a one-track

135

mind." Daran ignored his potential for a double-meaning, fascinated as she was in the insight he could provide into the workings of the mind of Drew Charles. "The senator has the ability to siphon out the crux of a matter, absorb it, then spit it back in improved form. He can turn on and off at will"—another double-meaning, she was to wonder later—"and has the uncanny ability to be on top of a score of things at once. You'll see, if you stick around!"

The only things she saw, however, before her flight back to Connecticut late Thursday evening, were the four walls of that office, the functional cafeteria where the aides habitually ate, and the silent comfort of her hotel suite, which saw her eyes closed for the night within fifteen minutes of her return there. At this point, Leo had pointed out, she was merely being introduced to the process. The physical demands would be minimal, with the bulk of the brainwork being ground out in the office. Later in the month, the legwork would begin.

Back in Connecticut, on familiar ground, Friday and Saturday passed as quickly. Once again Daran was in command—of her counseling sessions, of her Child Advocacy Project, of her garden, where green shoots had begun to spring up in healthy array. The silence at home pleased her, particularly after the pace of the work week just over. Drew's presence in the state for the weekend was deliberately pushed to the back of her mind, where it lingered with gnawing persistence. Despite his original invitation for her to accompany him on some of his rounds, the incident at the office that first morning had convinced her of his second thoughts. She was startled, therefore, to hear the deep voice at the other end of the phone at mid-afternoon on Saturday.

"Where have you been?" His anger surprised her even more than the call itself. "I've been trying you on and off for most of the day."

The return to her own world had emboldened her. Whereas in Washington she might have meekly explained, here there was defiance in her response. "I've been working—or had you forgotten. Your precious schemes have forced me to rearrange my own schedule. I conducted four counseling sessions this morning, and just returned from the library."

"What are you doing now?" Her own outburst had succeeded in stemming his irritation.

"I'm very busy enjoying what's called leisure. In case you don't know what that is," she rushed pertly on, making up in spades for the proper respect she had had to show him—not that there was reason for anything else—in Washington, "it's that time one sets aside to do nothing. Care to join me?"

The offer had been made tongue-in-cheek. When he accepted it, she was stunned. "I'll be right over." If her ears had heard properly, and her senses had interpreted similarly, there was an element of humor in the deep voice whose tone was abbreviated when the line went dead. Staring dumbly at the silent receiver in her hand, she had no idea what to expect. Here she was, in a snug T-shirt and a pair of faded denim cut-offs, barefooted as always in her own home, her hair curling randomly in the June humidity. What was she to do? Sheer obstinacy ruled out the possibility of changing into a more appropriate blouse and skirt; this was, after all, her own time. Their working arrangement had said nothing formal about weekends. If Senator Drew Charles planned to change that arrangement, he would simply have to give her fair warning!

The pitcher of iced tea had just about chilled by the time she padded into the kitchen. While half of her expected to receive a return phone call tipping the hoax, the other half listened for the sound of the car in her driveway. To her growing dismay, neither came. Puzzled and inexplicably annoyed, she carried her tall glass of tea to the patio, collapsing in the lounge chair, cool in the shade of the overhanging oak. It was in this position that the show began.

Her ear pricked up as, amid the gentle sounds of nature, came another sound, a more human one, that of footsteps —or, more accurately, a jogging pace—in the woods that extended for several acres in back of the house. Alarm quickened her pulse. The woods were private property, and were bounded only by private homes on all sides. When her widened eyes took in an unmistakably human shape emerging at a trot from the deep green depths, she gasped. Then slowly she expelled her breath in relief. For the shape had quickly taken on an identity and proved to be none other than Drew. Through the woods. Jogging. Bare to the waist and glistening with sweat. Clad in shorts and sneakers and gorgeous—positively gorgeous!

"How did you get here?" Daran shrieked as he slowed his pace and sauntered to where she sat now, forward and alert.

He was panting slightly, and paused to catch his breath and take a long, cool swig of her iced tea before explaining. "Through the woods."

"I can see that!" Her own drawl was exaggerated. "But how? From where?"

His gaze touched her directly. "My place."

"Through the woods?" she asked in disbelief. The tawny head of mussed hair nodded, moments before he drained the tea. "You live *here*?" The smugness in his expression was sufficient answer. "Why didn't you tell me you lived so close?"

"Does it matter?" As he stood before her, hands on hips, legs planted firmly apart, chest finally settling from the exertion of his jog, nothing seemed to matter but that magnificent body before her.

138

"No." The softness of her voice did not betray her thoughts, though her eyes must have done so. For Drew cast her a warning shot, then grabbed her hand to pull her up.

"Have you got a bathing suit somewhere?"

"Yes, but—" Her bewildered reply was cut short.

"Go get it. We're going for a swim."

"A swim? But where? I don't have a pool—"

It occurred to her suddenly that she did not need a pool if her neighbor had one. He saw the understanding in her eyes and passed up a retort of any kind, merely resuming his jogging, in place this time, and glancing at his watch. "Get a move on! We have to be at the Polo Grounds in Farmington by five; there's a group I have to meet with there. Then there's the Italian festival on Franklin Avenue, and, if we make it, the Hartford Stage Company's production of 'A Midsummer Night's Dream.' "

Incredulous amber eyes stared up at the bobbing figure. "But Drew, I can't go to those places wearing my bathing suit! You haven't given me much warning—"

The gray-eyed gaze pierced her intently. "You don't need much warning. Anything you choose will be fine. Any one of the outfits you wore in the office this week will do. Just—" he grinned, not missing a beat in his jogging, "—don't wear the leotard and tights I saw you in once. I may not be able to keep my hands off you." His growl was broken by spasmodic bouncing. And it took Daran not a minute longer to realize the purpose of his activity now. Turning, she smiled to herself; so he *had* caught her dance outfit, tired as he was that night. Changing into her swimsuit, she wondered just how he would react to it. Then, feeling more daring than she had in weeks, she pulled on a short terry cover-up, slipped into sneakers, and joined him.

It was a source of personal pride that she was able to

139

keep up with him on his jog back through the woods, though she suspected that his pace had slowed considerably, and for her benefit alone. The pool was as refreshing as the house was charming, set into the hillside opposite from hers, a contemporary structure decorated with taste and warmth.

"You do very well." He complimented her gallantly, propping himself against the side of the pool as she finished a slow crawl from the shallow end.

A slight submersion let her hair flow back over her shoulders as she came to rest not far from him. "What did you expect?" Her challenge was coated with fun, both the jog and the swim having worked off the tension that a hectic week had instilled in her muscles.

The afternoon sun sparkled against the gold and brown and auburn of Drew's hair, much as the water's glistening emphasized the steel-corded bands of his arms and shoulders. The latter lifted in a shrug as his lips curved mischievously. "Well, after all, you're almost thirty." Daran grimaced in spite of herself, bringing a loud guffaw from her companion. "It's really not so bad," he consoled her. "When is the big day?"

"Not until the end of July." One brief glance at the boyish enjoyment his teasing gave him—and she let him have his way.

"That long, hmm? You'd better make sure you get everything critical done before then. Just in case, you know . . ."

"Just in case *what?*"

Again he shrugged with endearing innocence. "Oh, you know, old age hits us all differently."

In a brief flash of conscience, Daran's thoughts flew to her mother's side. It was Mary Abbott's line about age, over and over again. Daran had spoken to her last week and had said nothing about her impending trip to Washington. What should she say when the phone call came tomorrow morning, as she knew it would?

"Hey." The voice had softened and was now inches from her ear. "I'm only kidding, Daran." It seemed only natural that, with the movement in the water that his body had caused, she should float against him. Reflexively she curved her arms around his neck for support.

"I was thinking of my mother," she explained in a near-whisper. At that moment his support was an emotional one as well. "She always jokes about her age. I really should call her more than I do."

"She must be very proud of what you are doing." It was a simple statement that opened up another can of worms.

A pained expression flitted across her gentle features before she could contain it. "She doesn't *know* half of it. We have our disagreements too. I only tell her as much as I think she can handle, or rather," she confessed softly, "as much as *I* can handle, once she gets going."

"Do you miss her?"

Her amber gaze covered the many miles between Simsbury and Cleveland before she spoke. "I think I miss the relationship we *don't* have. It might have been nice to be close."

Her words fell victim to another closeness, that of the chiseled features before her. Suddenly aware of the sinewed strength of his legs against her own and the wall of chest against hers, the force of her gaze came every bit to the present, as his had been all along. Without ceremony, he kissed her, pressing the strength of his lips against hers. It seemed a natural outgrowth of the emotional connection between the two. It seemed a natural outpouring of the respect each had slowly gained for the other. It was an inevitable meshing of bodies that had cried out, silently and with varying degrees of urgency, to each other

141

throughout the week, when the watchful eye of the public had precluded this particular type of closeness.

The water swirled about their limbs as he deftly propelled them to a more shallow point. His lips clung to hers all the while as her arms clung to his neck and shoulders. It was only when the buoyancy of the water gave way to the abrupt return of gravity that Daran realized she was being carried, gently and easily, toward the padded chaise that stood in the shadows at the far end of the pool.

A faint gasp escaped her lips when he eased her down, then stretched his length beside her. Of the fleeting impressions that came and went were ones of warmth and companionship, care and protection. It was so easy to talk to him—so easy to forget that other, more public side, and to know only the private man within. At that instant she realized that her need was no longer purely physical. Much as she prized herself an independent woman, she did crave a partner to be with, to talk with, and, yes, to make love with. All her fears seemed to fade into oblivion when Drew was around. His presence drove out all hesitancy, all reluctance. When he was near, in a private situation such as this, she was the only one in his mind, of that she was sure. He was interested in her, in her mind, her history, her ideas, as well as that more obvious interest to which he catered now.

For long moments they kissed. Then, when the flame of desire had been well kindled, each body moved to caress the other. For Daran, the touch of his skin against hers was a heady friction, its resultant heat scorching her. His lips in masterful possession of her own, he pulled her over toward him, his hand releasing the tie of her bikini top without faltering. As the thin slice of jersey fell to the patio amid the spring shedding of the weeping willow overhead, she arched closer, thrilling at the feel of her breasts against the water-cooled surface, finely matted in gold, of his

142

chest. When first his hands, then his lips plundered the ripeness of her creamy curves, she caught her breath. Drew spoke for them both.

"Have you any idea how much I want you?" The huskiness of his voice made its own statement, as tawny fingers found, then caressed with mindless devastation, the taut crest of her nipple. She could only writhe in futile attempt to eliminate all barriers between them. The firm muscles of his back flexed beneath her fingertips when he rolled over atop her. That his own arousal was as great as hers was no longer in doubt, that fact serving only to heighten her own pitch of desire. Then he paused, remembering all too clearly what Daran, in her wild state of ecstasy-driven oblivion, had pushed from his mind. The gray-eyed gaze that delved into her now asked the question. With her hands on his body, she answered. Groaning, he drew her close once more, but gently, as though she were something fragile. His breath stirred her dampened waves. "Tell me you want me to make love to you, Daran. I need to know that you *know* what you're doing."

But did she? It was clear that she wanted him, that some part of her needed him. But what about the long-range prospect? A virgin when Bill had so cruelly taken her on their wedding night, she had never been with another man. With Drew there was neither love nor marriage. If she surrendered to her own burgeoning desire, the basics of her value structure would be suddenly changed. Could she handle that?

"I only know what I'm doing at this very minute," she whispered hoarsely. "Yes, I do want you to make love to me. But as for why and what next, I don't know. You know what you do to me physically, Drew." Her accusation, gently as it had been offered, was met by a deep moan. When he made to move away, her tapered fingers circled his wrists to keep him near.

"Daran," he warned her from deep in his throat, "if I don't stop now, it will be too late." His gaze fell to caress the twin swells of her breasts, taking in the nudity which so tempted him. Then, sensing the urgency of his own plea, she let him go. Turning her back on both Drew and the pool, she listened for long moments as his rapid strokes slashed through the once-smooth surface. Her mind remained in the limbo into which it had fallen, to be raised up only when strong, wet arms took her shoulders and pulled her back against him again.

The sinewy forearms which crisscrossed her chest, covering breast and ribcage alike, held her closely, yet with none of the electricity that had been present before. "Listen, Daran," Drew crooned, the water from his body dripping freely onto hers, "someday it will be right for us. I think we both know that. But until it is, I'd rather wait. You've had one bad experience. When *I* make love to you, I want you to enjoy it as much as I do. You are very special." The last was a soft murmur against her hair, punctuated by a tender touch of his lips at her temple. It was small solace for the nagging ache in her loins, destined now to be unresolved. Yet, when he reached forward with one hand and retrieved the bikini top that had been discarded earlier, she made no move to restrain him. Once again he seemed to know better than she how to handle the situation.

It was only after she had put on her terry robe that he approached her once more. Placing an arm around her shoulder, he pulled her into step beside him, back toward the woods and her own house. "Please try to understand, Daran. There are so many things to be considered." Choosing his words with great care, his voice serenaded her until he unwittingly hit a wrong note. "I want to be very careful with you."

It was as though she had been slapped in the face. She

144

was, after all, one of his aides. And it simply wouldn't do to have a clandestine affair with her unless he knew that she was of the proper frame of mind not to make waves in the placid flow of his career. The pressure of teeth against her lip served to ward off the tears which had, so helplessly, sprung to her eyes. But why did it matter? What did it all mean anyway? Her relationship with Drew was marked for termination with the passage, hopefully, of his bill. His attentions toward her had all been directly or indirectly related to that relationship. In good faith she believed that his feelings for her were strong and good and honest. But his milieu could not be ignored, any more than could the fact that he had worked hard to get where he was and would do nothing to jeopardize that position.

"Pick you up in half an hour?" His soft words barely carried the weight to break into her thoughts. When her pale face turned dumbly up toward his, he repeated them, stroking her worry lines away with his finger. For a minute she thought he would question her on their cause. Thankfully he let it ride. A gentle kiss on her forehead sent her into her house to dress, while, lost in thought, he retraced his steps back through the woods. When the car rounded the drive thirty minutes later, she was ready.

It was as though, with the donning of more formal clothing, both relinquished the more carefree interaction of before. The evening, filled to the brim with activity as they passed from one event to the other, was to set a style which Daran would come to know well over the next weeks. In effect, she was Drew's assistant-companion on these return trips to his home state. Together they traversed the countryside, attending fair after fair, craft show after craft show. Summer in Connecticut was rife with such outdoor entertainment. At each there was a group of constituents to be met. Indeed, the scheming of Dwight Dewhurst and Stanley Morrow conspired to fill the sena-

145

tor's every minute, almost, with public appearances. If it wasn't a brief address to the environmentalists at Falls Village or an informal discussion on oil-spill control with the mariners at Bridgeport, it was a picture-taking session with the leaders of the Rose Festival at Norwich, the Country Dancers in New Haven, or the antique buffs in Lebanon. Occasionally the appearances broached a more touchy theme, such as the forceful plea for federal funding of the arts from the painters in Essex.

Through it all Drew handled himself as the consummate politician—cordial, interested, open-minded. The heat never fazed him as he stood for long periods of time in the sun watching one thing or another. Acutely aware of what was expected of him as the United States senator from the state, his patience seemed endless. It was only in those more quiet moments, usually as they drove, or were driven, from one spot to another, that frustration nagged at him.

"The problem is that constituents nowadays are one-issued. They feel strongly on their own, personal stand to the exclusion of all others. Those same people who, not more than thirty minutes ago," he explained as the air-conditioned interior of the car cushioned them from the line of tourist traffic in the center of Mystic, "begged for more money to restore this old ship or that, would be at my throat if I suggested that the government would have to tax them further to get that money. They want lower taxes with greater offer of services. It is an age-old dilemma—*I* don't have a solution!" In a rare gesture of discouragement, he combed his tanned fingers through the shock of hair which had, in the summer's heat, fallen over his brow. All Daran could do was to listen quietly, to act as a sounding board for his frustration. The solution to the dilemma was as evasive to her as to him.

146

It was to her surprise that she discovered her own enjoyment at accompanying him on these whirlwind tours of Connecticut. The heat *did* bother her, as did her feet, which were perpetually sore from standing for long periods of time, and her hair, which stubbornly escaped all attempted submission, to curl wildly about her head in wayward disarray. If she knew the appealing picture she made, standing with utter poise and innate beauty by the side of the tall and lean figure, she might have been shocked.

As it was, the pleasure was hard for her to pinpoint as she pondered it in those solitary times at her Simsbury home when Drew had returned to Washington. For starters, she enjoyed seeing the state from such an intimate viewpoint. The actual events they attended were only part of it; the other was the charm of the small New England towns through which they passed. About each, Drew had some gem of wisdom to offer. As they passed through the town of Plymouth, he pointed out Plymouth Hollow, where the earliest Seth Thomas clocks were made, one of which was the rosewood grandfather keeping guard in his own office. The picturesque town of Old Lyme sparked recollections of another Tea Party, one near-comparable to that more famous Boston Harbor event, but in Connecticut, when the local Sons of Liberty burned an entire shipment of tea which had been subject to unjust tax. Enfield was recognized as old Shaker territory, where, he informed her, the earliest marketing of garden seeds in small, handy envelopes took place.

They passed through Stafford Springs, whose sulphur-and-iron-enriched water had beckoned to many a president. The recreational lure of Norfolk tempted, with its lush greenery, its rambling bridle paths, its trout-filled streams—none of which the politician had the leisure time

147

to explore in any more than the most superficial manner. And the history of Wethersfield shone forth as their car passed through, with Drew's poignant depiction of the meeting held here between George Washington and the French, a meeting which set the foundation for the battle of Yorktown and the end of the Revolutionary War.

It was an education for Daran to travel with Drew and his party. But there was something more. There was—she struggled to identify it—a comfort at being near him. His attitude toward her was always warm and friendly, though far from the intimate and rarely straying from the brotherly. Yet he was *there,* and his very presence added some unknown element to her life.

Perhaps most indicative of her mood was its antithesis, the loneliness, the emptiness that set in late each Sunday evening of those weekends they spent together. Drew's plane would be aloft, winging its way from Bradley to Dulles. Though Tuesday morning, a mere thirty-six hours later, would find her once more in his Washington office, she missed him.

Though the weekends were bombarded with business and though he never sought to make use of the midnight hour for a suggestive rendezvous, there always managed to be—or Drew always managed to make—some small wedge of time for them to do something more private, more frivolous, more carefree.

There was a bicycle ride through Elizabeth Park early one morning, before the throngs descended to admire the assortment of roses lining the paths and arbors and trellises alike. As usual he gave her little warning, showing up on her doorstep with two bikes strapped to the back of a friend's sedan, giving her the minimum of time to dress and down a cup of coffee. But it was worth it. The air had been cool at that hour, the bugs still idle. Goldfish bobbed from the depths to the surface of the pond which, come winter, would be frozen over and skated on. As they pedaled, side by side, in quiet companionship, there was a peace about and within her that defied description.

Then, there was the sunset climb up Heublein Mountain, again when the worst of the crowds had begun to retrace their steps for the day. Together they surveyed the countryscapes of Avon and Simsbury, breathing in the panorama of the Farmington Valley region with smiles of appreciation. Again there was that peace, brief yet divine, and theirs to share. At times like these conversation was forgotten, as was, remarkably, all physicality. The natural romance of the setting went much deeper into Daran, holding her speechlessly entranced, until that familiar grasp of her shoulder turned her back toward home.

Most memorable in some respects was the fireworks display they attended on the Fourth of July. An annual happening at the boardwalk of New London's Ocean Beach, the show offered one after the other of the most breathtakingly colorful and intricately timed explosions. Darkness protected Drew's identity from the crowds gathered about them, as did his clothing—ultra-casual, verging on the knockabout—and his visored hat hid the full and instantly recognizable head of sandy-colored hair. In disguise, as he considered himself then, he felt freer and more relaxed, not quite as "on" all the time. Daran reflected his mood, responding readily to his impulse to gorge on hamburgers and hot dogs on the beach when the display had ended. It was, that night, as if they were two anonymous people enjoying one another and the world, totally alienated from the identities that would normally guide them. Much later she was to dream that these irresponsible moments could go on forever. On awakening, she knew better.

Drew was strong, sincere, and motivated to do things in the world. He was intelligent and dedicated, and thrived in the political arena. Though those "irresponsible moments" were precious to him, he could in no way live without the other. Daran had to accept that.

CHAPTER 7

It did grow easier to accept—this fact of Drew's love for his work—with the passing of each three-day period in Washington. For it was contagious. Viewing it from the inside, as she now did, Daran could not help but be swept up in the excitement. The enthusiasm of the staff, and that of the staffs of other senators, with whom she came in contact at meetings, in the corridors between offices, and in the cafeteria which they shared, could not be denied. Even given the limitations imposed by the legislative process itself, most notably the ever-constant need for modification to satisfy all parties, there was a deep sense of activism which permeated the Hill.

Following those initial sessions within Drew's suite of offices were the broader ones with potential witnesses in anticipation of the hearings. Each had to be located, contacted, then interviewed. There were more solitary hours spent at the library, chasing down one statistic or another, followed by long meetings back in the senator's office to discuss the findings. As much as his schedule allowed it, Drew sat in on these, listening quietly at first on the sidelines, then coming forward with his own opinion on whatever item it was they were dissecting that particular day. Throughout, she stuck to her claim that the bill had to go deeper than it had originally been designed to do. Drew and the other aides, usually Leo and the research assistants assigned him, and often John Hollings and Dwight Dewhurst, gave her free rein, challenging at times, agreeing at others. In some instances Drew himself yielded to her well-phrased and firmly founded pleas. It was a victory for her when he did so and instructed that the wording of some part of the bill be changed to include her suggestion; at those times she felt her presence in Washington to be truly fruitful. These small victories were not hers personally, but rather those of the Child Advocacy Project and the subjects it represented. If there was indeed a personal triumph, it was in the respectful smile Drew graced her with periodically, and which, in itself, buoyed her spirits. Occasionally words accompanied the smile; these were indelibly etched in her mind.

"Your point is well taken, Daran," he commented one morning, after an emotionally laden debate on the merits of guaranteeing every child the best of medical treatment for critical illnesses, such as leukemia. "There is that fine line where the control of the parents becomes hazardous when they disregard the advice of top doctors. Your suggestion of a panel to work with the courts in such situations is a good one. If you can come up with the guidelines for forming such a panel, we're all set."

The problem was one she had considered before. "The way I see it," she explained, making a point to include in her visual sweep all of those in the room and not only the handsome man who sat directly to her right, "there is a civic responsibility for participation on such a panel. The concept is similar to jury duty. If the courts approach it as such, I don't see how the medical field can ignore it."

Leo posed the follow-up. "Would you only include doctors on such panels?"

Again she was prepared. "Definitely not. If you have, say, five members of such a group, perhaps two or three should be from medicine, and the others should be from

152

the fields of psychology and social work. If there is a possibility that the wishes of the parents are going to be overruled, every aspect of the family situation has to be taken into account."

With a deliberate turn toward Leo, Drew spoke simply. "Write it in. Doctor's orders." The last was added with a twinkle in his eye and a tilt of the head in her direction. Daran would have beamed her delight, had it not been for the instant change of subject.

"Okay, Senator, that's it." Dwight Dewhurst broke into the discussion. As press secretary for the senator, it was his job to make the most of every opportunity for maintaining good public relations, both at home and in the capital. "I believe there is a group from the Connecticut Agricultural Cooperative waiting to see you. They'll be wanting a talk and some pictures."

Drew stood immediately, towering over them physically as he had done for the last half hour intellectually. "Let's not keep them waiting any longer, Dewey," he said to the man at the door, then turned back to the others for a last word. "Eastern Connecticut used to be heavily into dairy farming. There is still quite an interest there." A smile of good-natured amusement dazzled his staff, and Daran in particular, with its brightness. "Most people assume we Connecticut Yankees are fixated on insurance; we do throw them a twist every so often."

"Don't be so sure." It was the equally humorous tone of the press secretary again. "After the meeting with the farmers, you are scheduled to meet with the representatives of the major insurance companies. They want less restriction on their rates, needless to say."

For a minute Drew looked puzzled, surprised that he had forgotten about that later meeting. Checking briefly the small card in his pocket, he nodded. Even Daran knew, at this point, that there would be an aide with him on the way to that meeting, briefing him on the latest in rate restrictions from the legislative standpoint. But Drew seemed well informed himself. "It's a losing battle. They would like to increase their rates to provide money for housing rehabilitation. It's much the same issue as that with GCDC—do you remember, Daran? Theoretically it is very noble. The oldest and most rundown of the downtown Hartford buildings will be razed, and new modern structures built in their stead. The only problem is that this new housing is to be in the form of condominiums, which the poor people who are displaced can't come near to affording." With a deep sigh he walked to the door, leaving the others to pick up where they had left off on the Rights of Minors Act. Only Daran was aware of the almost imperceptible tug at the gold hoop of her earring as he passed by. It was a small gesture he had made before, the only sign that in any way indicated their own, more personal relationship. Each time he made it, it was done with such stealth as to be invisible to watchful eyes. Yet, each time, it sent an unfathomable quiver through her. And each time, she wondered whether he did this to other women, so precise was his aim and practiced the pressure he exerted. To her chagrin, she found herself surreptitiously examining earrings and the women who wore them, all the while wondering.

"Are you all going to the game tonight?" Drew's deep voice carried from the threshold.

Leo answered promptly. "Wouldn't miss it!" Grinning, his tone indicated that he would see that the others didn't. With that assurance, the senator left.

The game proved to be a softball match between the offices of Senator Charles and those of the senior senator from the state, Alan Higginston. Held in the park behind the White House known as the Ellipse, it was a boisterous gathering of the staffs, with the respective senators serving

154

as captain. Proudly wearing the green and white T-shirt that sported the ominous warning DREW'S DESTROYERS, Daran joined the fray merrily. The opposing team members, clad in blue and labeled, appropriately, HIGGINSTONS, were larger and more portly, on the whole, as was the renowned senior senator himself. Had it not been for the superior strategic ability and athletic prowess of Drew's team, the others might have won on sheer batting power. As it turned out, the Destroyers lived up to their name, fielding brilliantly, then taking the offensive in the fifth inning to overcome the opposition by a healthy nine-to-two margin.

As she replayed the event in her mind later that evening, Daran saw the consistency in Drew's character. A natural competitor, he weighed and balanced his opponent's strengths, then geared his game accordingly. Whether as pitcher, first baseman, or senator, all of which he played at some point in the game, he watched the other team as carefully as he executed his own moves. It was a demonstration of what Daran could expect in the weeks ahead, as the hearings on the Rights of Minors Act progressed and the goal of mark-up, then the final floor vote, approached.

Where once subcommittee hearings were held behind closed doors, now the proceedings were open. Each day the room was packed, as a bevy of senators, press representatives, guests, witnesses, spectators, and professional lobbyists filled the rows of chairs in this, the largest of the hearing rooms. Daran sat close behind Drew, as did Leo; other senators on the subcommittee, seated at the long curved table, were similarly fortified with their own pair or more of aides. As its chairman, Drew conducted the hearings, working from detailed papers before him—with which he was, however, thoroughly familiar—to question

155

each witness on that aspect of the issue of children's rights, or children's matters in general.

It was Daran's job, among others, to prompt Drew on points that were made that needed further clarification, or on inconsistencies in testimony that needed resolution. Additionally she was by now well versed in the positions of the other senators on the Rights of Minors Act, able to enlighten her senator as to the purpose behind a line of questioning one of the others had adopted. In actuality her role was more one of seeking instant additional information in response to the deeper questions which Drew himself raised in quiet whisper to either herself or Leo.

Not only was she fascinated by the process of the hearing, but she found herself, once again, duly impressed by the skill with which Drew conducted it. He was in full control; there was never a question of that. Of the many witnesses who testified, including various lawyers, judges, social workers, counselors, and even parents, he demanded the same even-keeled response, directing them pointedly, keeping them on the track when they strayed from it. On the handling of a couple, professional foster parents from the D.C. area, he was particularly sensitive.

Thoughts of their visit, Drew's and hers, to the home of that couple the week before was vivid in her mind as her eyes watched them now and her ears absorbed their testimony. It had been late in the day, in a half-hour span between the adjournment of the Senate for the day and a press conference which Drew held on the subject of solar energy. His dark blue sedan had taken them directly to their destination, a large converted three-family home in a less affluent section of the city. The Ferris family consisted of the parents and two boys of their own, to which had been added three other children on a foster basis, two of whom had been with them for four years and were indistinguishable in appearance and mood from the Ferrises' own. The other child, however, had been different, very different. Residing with them for only a few months, that child had been taken from his own home by the courts after repeated incidents of physical abuse had come to the attention of the local hospital. Now the bruises had healed —physically. The emotional state of the child was another matter.

Daran and Drew's observation of the children at play in the backyard had been unseen at first. At Mrs. Ferris's insistence, they had watched for several moments from the kitchen window. From all outward appearances, the children were happy and secure. Then the adults ventured into the backyard. Within an instant all the children but this one had run to the side of the woman they called mother; this one little boy, his eyes rounded and glued to Drew and Daran, steadily backed away from them, cowering visibly as he crept into a far corner of the yard.

"He's like this with any stranger," the kind woman had explained. "After being beaten to bits for the first three years of his life, you could say that he's gun-shy."

Gun-shy was a mild word for what they witnessed in that small boy that afternoon. As he tucked himself deeper into the corner, Drew slowly and carefully approached, talking softly all the while as though nearing a wounded and terrified animal. Now, as the woman told the subcommittee of her experiences with similarly abused children over the years, Daran recalled how triumphant had been the gleam in Drew's eye when he finally returned to them, the youngster calmly propped atop his shoulders. In later months similar moments of victory, though perhaps more far-reaching, would be no more heartfelt.

During the few weeks that the hearing was in progress, Daran further rearranged her schedule in Hartford to allow for her attendance in Washington until noon on Fridays, when the hearings were adjourned for the weekend. As always, she marveled at the way Drew moved deftly from one activity to the next, always gracious, always patient, always in superb senatorial form. He greeted a group of retired teachers from Willimantic with the same enthusiasm that he addressed the National Association of Hardware Manufacturers, of which many members were constituents from Connecticut.

Though his outward approach to Daran remained reserved, with no further private tête-à-têtes or dinners, he kept her by his side for more of the time than her specific role required. For this she was grateful, though, for as the weeks passed, the gnawing frustration for a more intimate relationship grew. Other than the occasional twinkling glance, tug of the ear lobe, or light hand on the waist, however, he made no moves. If he was at all disturbed by this pretense of propriety, she couldn't tell. That he should —that they *all* should grow more tense as the hearings drew to a close and the final mark-up was completed, was perfectly natural. After all, the floor fight would be the next hurdle to jump, and it promised to be a tough one. But when he left word that she should wait in his office for him to return from the Senate floor the day after the completion of the mark-up, she was perplexed.

For practical purposes her work was done. The mark-up had produced a new wording of the bill that she found to be surprisingly strong and much to her liking. Having been put together in subcommittee following the hearings, the new bill was sure to pass on through the full committee and be put on the Senate schedule for a vote. From here on in, she was primarily a spectator. Now, arriving early at Drew's spacious office, she listened to the squawk box that relayed the on-going discussion on the Senate floor. There was more than a little regret that her time in Washington was nearing its end. Perhaps this was what he had wanted to see her about—a good-bye.

"Ah, good! You're here!" Half expecting that the beautifully familiar voice had come from the small desk speaker, Daran bolted in surprise when a firm hand settled momentarily on her shoulder before he strode past her to the other side of his desk.

The sparkling amber of her gaze reflected her confusion. "*You're* here! I-I thought you were still on the Senate floor."

The devastating grin threatened to further discompose her, but he went on to explain. "You must have heard the buzzers too. There was that one important roll call. Now, however, my colleagues are stuck with a pretty boring battle of words between Hodgkins and Mareno; it could go on for hours. And I was in no mood to stay."

Relaxing once more in the comfort of the large leather chair, Daran spoke freely. "It's odd how often the chamber is nearly deserted. It must be disillusioning for those guests in the galleries who come to see government at work. They see a handful of senators babbling on and on."

Having listened to her with an indulgent smile, he eased himself against a corner of the desk, temptingly close to where she sat. Now an arched brow chided her. "You should have been there an hour ago. It was as busy as it gets. But I see what you mean. It is pretty ludicrous at times." He paused, stroking the roughness of his lean jaw absently. Then, his gaze caught her once more. "The *whole* thing has something pretty ludicrous to it, if you stop to think about it. As the years have passed, senatorial staffs have grown larger. With the increase in the number of aides each senator has, there has been an increase in the amount of work—committee assignments and so on—he can handle. So he is inundated with issues, and finally has to hire more staff. It's a never-ending circle—"

"Which you love!" The softness of her voice as it interrupted his revealed her sincerity, as did her expression. Drew's gentled in its wake.

"Yes," he admitted, quietly but firmly, crossing his arms over his chest. "Which I love."

That was the bottom line, as she had known it would be. Now, strangely, she was at a loss for words. Silently the two stared at one another, the faint drone of the squawk box the only sound in the room. For a minute she saw the hint of tension that had lain beneath the veneer of his carved features during the past week. Then, it had been attributed to the climax of the hearing; now, that conclusion was in doubt.

"Are you pleased with the outcome of your work?" he finally asked. The piercing of his eyes enforced the personal nature of the question.

"It's *your* work," she corrected him lightly, "and, yes, I am pleased. I'm not quite sure why you let Leo include some of my very pointed suggestions though." There was skepticism in her soft accusation which he sought immediately to overcome.

"It's all a matter of compromise, Daran. If we aim higher than we are actually willing to settle for, we have something to bargain with."

Her nod signaled her understanding and agreement. Once more a silence settled in the air, broken only by the dim cackle of the transmitter. Their eyes locked and held. Though his thoughts were an enigma to her at that moment, her own were not. She had come to feel very strongly about this man; where she was to go from here, she was not sure.

His oath preceded a totally symbolic gesture of gruffly leaning toward the squawk box and shutting out all sound of the Senate. A strong hand reached toward her, and she took it, allowing herself to be drawn from her seat to stand between his legs, which were casually draped over a cor-

160

ner of the desk. With the very softness she had missed so desperately over the last weeks, he kissed her, holding her quivering body close to his, pressing a hand on the small of her back to arch her ever nearer. Drawn into the vortex of his appeal, she coiled her slender arms around his neck, returning his kiss with every bit of the feeling she could not yet identify. It was only the sudden opening of the office door that broke the spell.

"Drew, oh, excuse me." Red-faced, John Hollings remained at the door, tactfully giving the two an opportunity to compose themselves. The fact that he did not leave at once spoke for the urgency of his mission.

Setting her back from him, though not releasing the armhold on her shoulder, Drew stood. "What is it, John?" Suddenly he sounded tired, more so than she had ever remembered him being.

"It's on those confirmation hearings, Drew. Brown and MacIntyre want to know where you stand. They're trying to schedule the thing for sometime next month."

The senator inhaled deeply, dropped his hand from her shoulder, then slowly exhaled. "Give me a minute, John. I'll be right with you. And . . . are those people from Avon here yet?" He looked down to explain softly to Daran. "There's been an uproar about polluted wells in Avon— illegal dumping of petroleum waste." Then the gray eyes shot back to his administrative assistant.

The latter put him at ease. "Not yet. Give them another fifteen minutes or so." Without further word, he stepped back and closed the door, leaving Daran and Drew alone again.

Drew's sandy head shook as a hand massaged the muscles at the back of his neck. "I'm sorry, Daran. That was bad timing." Was he worried that John had seen something? she wondered.

"That's all right," she began in an attempt to make light

of the situation. "It was just a good-bye kiss. I have to be leaving."

Sharp gray eyes speared her. "I thought you were staying until tomorrow."

His near anger puzzled her. "I am. But I'm tired. I'll just be going back to the hotel for an early evening." At that moment a lump formed in her throat. Swallowing it convulsively, she grabbed her bag and headed for the door. "Bye-bye." It was a mere whisper, spoken without another glance back at the leanly masculine figure behind her. John's presence just outside the office precluded any further conversation. A deliberately paced walk took her out of the suite, down the corridor and the stairs, and out to the street, where the tears that had brimmed slowly trickled down her face. Sunglasses were her only foil.

Alone finally in her room, she gave way to sobs, venting an emotion whose depth terrified her. What were her feelings toward this man with whom she had worked for the past two months? Respect and admiration were givens; she had seen him at work, serving his state and the country in the most outstanding way. But adoration—that was something in a different league. Yes, she adored Drew Charles. But then, didn't most of his female constituents? He held a charismatic quality so few leaders possessed; she had fallen prey to it.

There was only one rationalization for the future. Tomorrow morning an Eastern shuttle would take her back to her home in Connecticut. From there, if she wished, she could watch the comings and goings of Senator Drew Charles through the press. Her own work would consume her once more, as she willed it to, and there would be nothing but fond memories of this phenomenally exciting time in her life.

Armed with this resolution, she relaxed beneath a warm shower, threw on her robe, then ensconced herself in an armchair to watch the evening news. Within minutes a knock at the door startled her.

"Yes?" she called out, slowly approaching it.

Low and clear, the voice seared through the door, then her. "It's me. Drew."

An unsteady hand unbolted the door and turned the knob. His face was in shadow, the hall light dim behind him. "I'm not dressed!" she apologized, distraught at having been caught in such a state, praying that her eyes did not reflect her great distress. "I didn't expect you."

"That's obvious." The element of tension was thick in his tone. "May I come in?"

Gesturing with her hand, she stood back to let him pass, closed the door, then headed for the bedroom. "I'll get something on—"

"No. You don't really have to change. I won't be that long." There was a flatness to his expression that disturbed her and she was unable to interpret. Oblivious to her quandary, he dropped into the nearest chair and proceeded to watch the rest of the news program.

Unsureness held her rooted to the floor for long moments before she finally allowed herself to take the chair opposite his. Fatigue, tension, irascibility all seemed to have taken over his normally placid body. Her amber eyes beamed their concern as she watched him, but he was oblivious to that too. It was only when the final credits appeared on the screen that he reached forward, switched off the set, and turned to her.

"I'm expected at a reception at the Portuguese embassy by nine o'clock. I just wanted to give you this." The hand that had taken refuge in his jacket pocket now emerged bearing a small box, wrapped simply in white with a delicate red bow.

Daran stared at it in astonishment. Words escaped her in the confusion that engulfed her. What was this? A proper send-off? Was this a custom for all of his workers whose tour of service had ended?

The tanned hand nudged the gift toward her. "Take it. It's a birthday present."

Hands trembling, she followed his instructions. Unwrapping the present was a minor issue; stemming the tears that threatened when she saw its contents was something else. Her voice was barely audible when finally she spoke.

"They're magnificent. Drew, you should never have—"

"Try them on." It was an order as forceful as any he had given her.

With some difficulty, considering her unsteadiness, she removed from her ears her usual gold hoops and inserted the small diamond studs that had been in the box. In lieu of a mirror, her eyes flew to Drew's. His smile of satisfaction, the first spark of pleasure since he had arrived, told her all she wanted to know. Yet, at a loss for other conversation, she asked anyway.

"How do they look?"

Her face was radiant in his gaze, now suddenly warm and melting, and he answered her softly. "*You* look beautiful. To hell with the earrings." Then he paused, as though to make a decision. "Daran, I know that you have to get back tomorrow. You've been wonderful, rearranging your schedule for us this summer. But I wonder if I might ask you a final favor?"

The strangely beseeching glaze that coated his entire expression turned her stomach to putty. "Of course." She shrugged gently, smiling through her bewilderment.

"The floor fight—I'd like you to be here for that, and for the final vote on the bill. You've been . . . so much a part of it, that I want you to see it through to the end."

Her eyes flooded once more, but she managed a bright smile. "I'd love that!"

164

Drew's tawny eyebrows lifted in inquiry. "You can manage your own things around it?"

Dark waves bobbed about her robe collar as she nodded. "Very easily. The month of August is pretty dead anyway. And I had planned to take some time off then."

As though a weight had been lifted from his shoulders, he stood to leave. "I'm glad. And . . . happy birthday, Daran!"

Shyness attacked her suddenly. "It's not until Saturday."

"But you'll be home by then. This is *our* celebration." When he took her into his arms, she lifted her mouth to thank him properly for the gift and, more important, the thought behind it. For such a busy person to have remembered this occasion touched her more deeply than she could have imagined. The iron band of his arms held her to him, his hands moving up and down her back, molding her firmly against his body.

"My God!" he exclaimed. "I've got to go!" The breathlessness of his voice told her that he had discovered the full state of her undress. Yet he indulged himself a moment longer, pressing his lips gently to hers as he caressed her body a final time. Flames of desire whipped through her, threatening to spark an explosion at the core of her femininity. When he released her, she would have called him back, had he not headed straight for the door and left. It was much as she had done that afternoon, though his own feelings were as yet unknown to her.

The only thing she *did* know was that, given this reprieve and the hope of seeing him in less than a month's time, it would be a very lonely few weeks she had to survive first.

CHAPTER 8

The issue of survival went much further, however, than the next eighteen days. It would be much too easy to fall in love with Drew Charles—if she hadn't already. Such was the gist of her contemplation as she resumed the life she had once found so pleasant. With the exception of classes, which were suspended for the summer, work awaited her. Glen was at her office more often than ever, wanting the latest rundown on chances for passage of the Rights of Minors Act. She spoke regularly with Hamilton Brody at Trinity, George Imlatt at the hospital, and, of course, every Sunday, her mother. The emotional needs of her clients remained high, demanding her usual intensity of concentration during counseling sessions. And there was always some new emergency crying out for attention.

Yet, despite the rapid pace, there was an inevitable letdown from the excitement of life in Washington to the more plebeian existence in Connecticut. Where once she had thrived on its orderliness, now she missed the other and, most specifically, the spontaneous activity that Drew's presence had assured. More than once she looked up from work in her garden to study the adjoining woodlands, listening for that telltale footstep on the dried twigs, watching for that sunbaked torso and the compelling face above it.

But all was quiet. To her knowledge Drew was in Washington for the entire period, foregoing the trips home, which had been more frequent in the past few months, to concentrate on the inundation of legislative work that always preceded the approach of the session's end. Neither did he send word of any sort to her, though she chided herself for hoping, much less expecting, that he would. After all, he was a very important individual, one sought out by many other than herself. And she had already gotten far more than she bargained for.

Her soul-searching led to one conclusion—she was playing with fire in prolonging the relationship by having agreed to return to Washington for the floor fight. In the first place, for every additional day she spent in the nation's capital, there was the heightened risk of running into Bill. At the start, this thought had hounded her, until she quickly discovered the very specific demarcation between the House of Representatives, of which her former husband was now a member, and the Senate, in whose exclusive circles she had remained during her visits. Complacency had come on the heels of relaxation on this score. After all, she neither ate meals out nor dated, either of which situation might have led to an accidental meeting. In truth, her social inactivity had had not as much to do with fear of seeing Bill as with distaste for the offerings. More than once, other legislative assistants, including the subtly lecherous Leo Alteris, had asked her out. Her own mind, however, could think of spending her own free time with but one man—and he walked a very, very straight line.

There was also the very great risk of falling even harder for Drew than she already had. Knowing how futile it was to expect anything more from him than he had already given, she refused to allow herself to consider in detail the full extent of her attachment. Love had no role in Washington; it was a wasted exercise to consider it. But the

167

heart had ways of overriding the mind on all too many occasions. This she knew intuitively. Actually, with Bill, it had been the other way around. Fully aware that she was not enmeshed in blinding love, marriage to Bill had simply seemed right at the time. She was attracted to him, both physically and emotionally, and the kind of life he promised was everything she had always dreamed of. It had been a rude awakening to learn that those things meant absolutely nothing without love and respect between their partners. The glimpse she'd had of Drew, both as a senator and as a person, was beautiful, and she knew, in her heart, that she did have his respect. Love was another thing. If late hours, frequent separations, and the ever-present stress of the limelight were to be borne, there had to be love.

On impulse she phoned her mother one evening. "Are you all right, sweetheart?" she had asked quickly, surprised at receiving such an unexpected call.

Daran had as quickly reassured her. "I'm fine, Mother. I just felt like saying hello and talking for a bit." Up until this point, she had said nothing to her mother about her summer activities. From the silence on the matter, gossip had not spread quite as far as Cleveland. For Mary Abbott was not one to stand on ceremony; had she heard anything, she would have surely asked long before now.

"Well, what have you been up to? Anything exciting?" The woman was obviously pleased at having heard from her daughter on such an impromptu basis, and it was this warmth of tone that prompted Daran to elaborate on her excitement. Her mother was thrilled. "So you've been in Washington all this time?" she asked enthusiastically when Daran hnd finished outlining her role in shaping the Rights of Minors Act.

"Well, only for a few days each week." Daran was fast to qualify the impression. "I still have these other things going here—you know, my counseling and the Advocacy Project."

"But Washington! That's right in the middle of it, dear! Your Senator Charles has built quite a reputation. We hear his name mentioned often. How was it—working for him?"

How was it working for him? It had been the most exciting, the most inspiring, the most rewarding thing that Daran had done to date. "Very interesting, Mother," she replied noncommittally. "He is bright and a hard worker. Needless to say, his staff is kept on its toes. He pounced on me more than once for not having four sources, rather than three, to corroborate my claims."

"Hmm, sounds like an ogre." The return quip was offered with good humor on the part of Mary Abbott; she had seen enough of politicians to know that while each had his smiling side, there lurked, somewhere beneath, the makings of a scowl.

Too quickly Daran spoke up in Drew's defense. "Oh, no. He was really a good boss. I never mind working my tail off for a good cause."

"And his is one? I take it you changed your original opinion?" The grin on her mother's face was evident in her tone.

"Yes, Mother. It was a good cause. And, yes, I did change my original opinion." Without elaborating and having made enough of a confession for the time being, Daran veered off on a tangent. "Tell me, Mother. How do *you* do it? How do *you* survive the whole rat race of politics? How has your marriage come through the past twenty-some-odd years intact?" It was a question that Daran had never before quite had the courage to ask as bluntly.

There was a brief silence on the line as her mother

contemplated the answer. When it came, however, its spontaneity was as evident as its honesty.

"I love Hugh. We *make* it work. Keep in mind, of course, dear, that he is not quite as much on the pigeon's stoop as one of those senators or representatives. In some ways Hugh has more power from backstage, where he operates." Daran knew all too well what she meant, and, although she didn't approve of her stepfather's tactics all the time, she had to acknowledge that he got things done. "And, though you may not have known it at the time," her mother continued softly, recalling that time herself, "there was many a day back there when I wondered whether it was worth it. But I *did* love Hugh. And I was willing to fight to keep him. So I turned myself into the kind of person who could function by his side, day in and day out."

A year ago, perhaps even as recently as a few months ago, Daran might have scoffed at the woman as the embodiment of the downtrodden female. But there was nothing downtrodden about Mary Abbott. And now, for some reason, her daughter had mellowed. "Didn't it ever bother you—not having an identity of your own?"

A gentle laugh danced along the wire. "Oh, but I did. I had and still have the most interesting and exciting life that I could have imagined. And I am Hugh's wife and your mother. No other woman in the world can make that claim!"

In that instant Daran's admiration of her own mother was at an all-time high. Though her own aspirations were quite different, she had to respect the woman, not only for her determination but for her confidence, her pride, and the devotion which welled so readily within her. "Do you ever wish—" Daran's own voice softened to a more vulnerable chord "—that you could just go away somewhere, you and Hugh, to live out your lives together, away from

170

all the hullabaloo?" A vision of Drew's father appeared before her eyes, and she recalled the tragic death of the woman who might have happily shared that isolated cottage in the woods with him, had she been able to survive the years before.

Her mother's response brought her back to the telephone receiver in her hand. "I wish *that* at some point, some small point, of every day of every year. But it passes. After all, this *is* our life. It's what we love doing. For the small satisfaction of escaping some of those pressures, we would be left with a very peaceful shell of a life."

Daran remained silent for a long time. Finally she sighed. "I wish we had talked of this years ago." Her voice was quiet, her words heartfelt. This closeness she felt now for her mother was gratifying. "It might have saved me an awful lot of anger over the years. I never quite understood . . ." The cut in her voice reflected so many different thoughts that she wondered if, in fact, she understood anything more now. But Mary Abbott's follow-up startled her, pushing all sorting out into the future.

"Daran, are you trying to tell me something? Is there someone?" With a gasp, she added, "Are you seeing Bill again?"

"No!" Vehemence gave strength to her denial. "I haven't seen Bill. It's just that I realize now that I went into that whole thing with the wrong frame of mind."

"Does Bill know you've been in Washington?" Daran was too wrapped up in her own thoughts to sense her mother's misinterpretation.

"Not that I know of. I've kept pretty much to myself except for work with Drew and his staff."

Her mother chose her words carefully. "How long will you be in Washington in August?"

"I'm not sure. A week, maybe more. Why?"

"Will you be able to come visit us at all before classes

171

begin again in September?" With the skill of the gracious conversationalist, Mrs. Abbott changed the subject.

Again Daran missed the strategy of the move. Again it was unusual for her. In the past she had been skeptical of every word her mother said, and her every motive for saying it. Now, however, her mind was otherwise occupied.

"Ah, I'm not sure, Mother. I'd like to try to fly out sometime right around Labor Day, but it will pretty much have to be last minute. There's so much else happening."

Indeed there was, both in her own mind and in her life. As she hung up the telephone several moments later, she wondered about this enlightening conversation she had held with her mother. Her mother had, quite inadvertently, given her the key concepts to help explain the failure of her marriage. It was no longer enough to blame Bill for his insensitivity, his egotism, his physical brutality. Daran had herself to blame, in part. She should have never agreed to marry Bill in the first place. Perhaps, had she known then more of her mother's deeper feelings, she might have foreseen the disaster. She had not loved Bill enough to mold her life to his. She had had too many hopes and dreams of her own to be able to agree to Bill's demands of total submission. It was a match doomed from the start.

What, then, about the future? Suppose her feelings for Drew grew even stronger. Suppose he held more than just a fond regard for her. What then? Could they forge a life together, welded around both his political career and her own as a psychologist? Then she caught herself short. Drew did *not* love her. The silence of her telephone line gave witness to that! Yet, she couldn't help but go into her bedroom, remove the leather jewelry case from her dresser, and put the exquisitely glittering diamond studs into her ears. It was a ridiculous picture—the grace of the earrings in comparison to her ultracasual shirt and shorts. Yet it gave her some unfathomable solace to look, to touch, to remember.

If Daran thought that the Senate fight would be a token one, she was greatly mistaken. When she arrived in Washington, on the arrangements of the ever-faithful but strangely harried John Hollings, the office was abuzz with meetings and huddles, phone calls and executive sessions. It was the third week in August. The Rights of Minors Act was to be opened for discussion on the Senate floor two days after she arrived. Immediately she was made privy to the score of amendments that other senators planned to offer to modify the Act to their specifications.

Where she had expected simply to be a spectator, suddenly she found herself fully in the midst of the fray, studying amendments, listing pros and cons, examining, along with Leo and the others, just what part of the original bill could be sacrificed for the purpose of bargaining.

Having been without sight or sound of Senator Drew Charles for the better part of three weeks, his appearance, that first morning of her return to the Capitol, was jolting. Magnificent as ever in the aura that enveloped his entire being, he was nonetheless tired, more tightly coiled, and shorter of temper than when she had seen him last. The wan smile she received when he spotted her across the room was a pale imitation of the warm welcome she would have preferred. But it was the work that quickly engulfed them all, such that Daran had no time to brood about the strengths or weaknesses or deeper meanings of one pitiful smile.

Again she found herself by Drew's side for much of the day. The hurried pace from his office to the underground subway, then on to the Senate floor became a routine, every minute in transit used for discussion of the item to

173

be discussed when they arrived. From her post with other legislative aides at the rear of the chamber, Daran studied Drew as he managed the bill, delivering the powerful arguments which she had herself fought for in weeks past. In the end, some of the points fell prey, of necessity, to the survival of others. As Drew had explained, it was a matter of compromise. The primary goal was that the bill pass. Opposition was heavy, as it was with any far-reaching new concept. When, after days of arguing back and forth, the roll call vote was taken, she quaked in anticipation.

Waiting beside John Hollings, as each of the senators' names were individually called, she chatted softly with the administrative assistant. "He is stupendous out there, isn't he?"

The beam of her amber gaze focused sharply on the tall, sandy-haired man who awaited his turn to cast his vote. She was oblivious to John's own study of her, which took in the warm pink of her cheeks, the fullness of her smile, and the glowing pride that her eyes expressed. "Yes, Daran, he's quite a man. But you're going to have to do something about his orneriness. It's been terrible lately." The gleam of humor in his eye told only half of the story; the other half John Hollings was too loyal to divulge.

Recalling the tension she'd seen herself too often in him, she laughed softly. "He'll ease up once this is over. It's taken so much of his time and energy."

For long moments, the other continued to scrutinize her as the vague murmur of voices in the background registered the fast-sealing fate of their love-child. "What is the count, Leo?" He turned suddenly to the man on his other side.

"This is a hair-raiser. The tally is thirty-three to twenty-seven. We have a supposed majority of those senators still to vote, but you never can tell until the final call."

Daran heard enough to set her pulse to racing. This was

the moment she had waited for, had worked for for the past three months. All three of Senator Charles's staffers stood silently, motionless, as, one by one, the votes came in. When the 57 to 43 result was announced, declaring victory for the Rights of Minors Act and all who would be one day affected by it, she nearly burst with joy. Proper decorum was the operative mode, however—until they reached the protective walls of the offices once more. Then glee rang out loud and clear. It was both a triumph for the children of the country and for the future standing of the junior senator from the state of Connecticut!

"Were you pleased?" Drew asked her later, when the maître d' had seated the two in a quiet corner of one of the most chic and exclusive restaurants in Washington. It was the very first restaurant she had eaten at in the capital, aside from her hotel coffee shop and the Senate cafeteria. Even now some doubts remained. But the joy of the victory was too great to be blemished by her lingering fear of running into Bill. And, she had reasoned with very mixed feelings, this would be her last night in Washington.

There was no hesitancy in her response, neither in words nor in the spontaneous smile that softened the slim line of her face. "Of course! The bill *had* to pass. It's what we've been working for for so long."

Looking positively handsome, if still a bit tired, Drew eyed her with gentle chiding. "No, I mean the bill itself. Were you pleased with the final version?"

As she pondered his question, her tapered fingernail absently rubbed the jagged edge of the elaborate menu. "I might have liked to have some parts stronger." She grinned sheepishly, recalling her own vehement arguments. "But, on the whole, it's a good bill. Where does it go from here?"

Leaning back in his chair, he explained the rest of the

process of turning the bill into law. "The House has to act on it, one way or the other. If the form they`pass is different from this one, a joint committee will be formed, consisting of representatives of both houses of Congress. Hopefully they will reach a compromise, enabling final passage of the bill."

As she absorbed the depth of his gray gaze, locked with her own, Daran recalled how astonished she'd been when, after the festivities in the office that afternoon, Drew had drawn her aside and insisted she join him for dinner.

"But I haven't anything to wear!" she had protested feebly, remembering one other occasion when she had thrown him a similar argument.

"You've got two hours," he had growled back good-naturedly. Mercifully they were out of earshot of the others. "Buy something."

That was exactly what she had done. Enjoying herself to no small extent, she had purchased a flowing dress of aqua silk, long-sleeved, deep V-necked, nipped in at the waist, and perhaps the most exquisite dress she ever remembered owning. The approval in Drew's eyes when he picked her up at her hotel suite was instant reward for the splurge. His own appearance was, as always, breathtaking—his dark suit and tie, and the contrasting light shirt that fit his leanly muscular lines to perfection, his sandy hair groomed carefully, his freshly shaven cheeks a constant temptation to touch. But it was his eyes, with their power to melt and to magnetize, that held her then, as they continued to do now.

"So, what is the final verdict, Daran? Have you enjoyed Washington?" The light lilt to his voice was at odds with the intensity of those eyes.

"Yes," she began slowly, treading her way carefully as she went on. "I've enjoyed every minute of it. It has been a truly educational experience, not to mention the satisfaction of being able to go back home and report favorably to the Advocacy Project executive board."

Mention of her return to Connecticut was purposely ignored. "You haven't seen much of the town. Why haven't you dated?" The bluntness of his query startled her, as did the faintly accusative lowering of his brows.

"I really haven't had the time." She shrugged, feigning nonchalance as she prayed he would leave that particular issue alone. This time her prayer was not answered.

"I happen to know that you've had invitations."

"And how would you know that?" Her chin tilted a bit higher in a return of her long-forgotten indignation.

"It's my job, Daran," he answered patiently, if evasively. "My staff is a key to my success on the Hill. Assuming that they have the gray matter to start with, they will work up to par and beyond only if they are happy. I try to keep on top of what's going on."

Nodding her head, she looked down at her menu. The loose darkness of her wavy hair fell around her face in a soft foil for her innermost feelings. By the time she had made a decision on what to order, her composure was, once more, intact. If Drew had wanted to pursue the matter, he must have thought better of it. It was only after he had given her order, then his own, to the waiter that he spoke again, this time on a more neutral topic.

"When do your classes start again?" His eyes fell to her lips, then quickly caught themselves and lifted once more, leaving her momentarily breathless but otherwise poised.

"Not until the middle of September. There are some department meetings beforehand, though. I'm planning to teach a new seminar this fall."

Under Drew's gentle and interested prodding, she described the proposal that had been approved last spring. His enthusiasm for the new course seemed as genuine as hers, by the time their food arrived. The rest of the dinner

177

proceeded with easy conversation and superb cuisine. To her own elaboration of her fall schedule, Drew added a summary of the work he would be doing during the next few weeks. With the exception of one sticky confirmation hearing, which prompted a return of the worry lines to his bronzed forehead, he told of a schedule of hearings, meetings, lectures, and two trips.

As they lingered over coffee, Daran wondered what was to come in the saga of her heart. The warmth of the coffee as it penetrated the inner chill that suddenly gripped her did little to sustain her. The presence of this dynamic man across the small table from her became torturous, wanting as she did to be with him, knowing as she did the unlikelihood of that. As though sensing her train of thought, he leaned forward, forearms on the table. In the atmospheric intimacy of the restaurant, his nearness sent quivers through her.

"I'm glad you wore the earrings. They sparkle in tune with those amber eyes of yours." Deeply husky, his tone stole rational thought from her. More than anything she wanted to forget all else and surrender totally to him. More than anything she wanted him to help her, once and for all, overcome the past and its lingering fears. More than anything she wanted *him*.

The silence between them was soft and gentle, a soul-reaching interaction as loud as the thunderous hammering of dual pulse beats. Words were superfluous to the visual give and take. When his long fingers stretched to touch the tip of her earlobe, it was in unspoken encouragement of her thoughts. The slow smile that curved her lips was extended to his. It was a beginning. Then she froze. A movement in her peripheral vision caught her attention, and she shifted her gaze to the face at a table not far from theirs. It was Bill! After all this time and on the first occasion she had dared take the chance as blatantly, her worst fear had become reality. The man she had wished never to see again had now, by virtue of his mere presence, destroyed the moment.

"What is it, Daran?" All huskiness had evaporated, replaced by a deliberate evenness.

With monumental effort she dragged her eyes away from the horror of nightmares relived in those few short instants of recognition. "I-I think I'd like to go b-back to the hotel now." Eyes averted from both men now, her hand took her purse and she stood quickly, waiting only long enough for Drew to stand before heading for the door.

No word was spoken until they were in the car again. "What happened back there?" he demanded, his anger and frustration barely held in check. "I thought—"

"I'm sorry, Drew." Frantically she rubbed her forehead in attempt to settle herself. But the shock of seeing her former husband was too great. "I just have to go back. It's something . . . very personal." No more than a whisper, her words seemed to infuriate Drew.

Jaw tensed, fingers white-knuckled on the steering wheel, he sped through the evening traffic, pulling up with a lurch in front of her hotel. Inhaling deeply, she took the hand that was offered her and submitted to its punishing grip as he helped her from the car and drew her into the lobby, up the elevator, then down the corridor to her door. Searching her soul for the words to explain, she could find none. A shaking hand fumbled for the key, then relinquished it to Drew's steadier one. She passed ahead of him into the living room, head bowed, innards quivering. Seeing Bill was bad enough; but at that particular moment . . .

"Look, Daran. I'm headed for Montreal in the morning. A plane will be at my disposal. If you were planning on taking the shuttle back to Bradley anyway, let me drop

179

you there on the way. It will give us some time to talk."
His form seemed to tower against the door frame as she
turned to look at him. Maybe a good night's sleep would
give her the courage to explain her sudden turnoff.

When she raised her eyes to his, he held them closely,
studying, delving, trying to read into her soul. To her
dismay he stiffened. His voice was a low order when he
finally spoke.

"Be ready at seven-thirty. We'll have breakfast when
we're airborne."

This time he did wait to hear her agree, as if he half-
suspected she would bolt before dawn. The eyes that
pierced her were cold, hard steel, the shoulders were as
rigid.

"That's fine," she heard her own voice whisper tremu-
lously. Whether it was a smart move, she did not know,
but she simply did not have the strength to refuse.

The night's sleep was neither good nor restorative for
either of them. When Drew appeared on her threshold
promptly at seven-thirty, his glower spoke above all else.
Daran had slept very little; her makeup barely disguised
that fact. They picked up where they had left off the night
before—in a heavy silence that cast its gloomy mantle over
an already overcast day. Her only surprise came when
they boarded the small plane and learned that, aside from
its crew, they were the only passengers. Drew seemed not
at all perturbed. His arms were laden with bags and papers, briefcases and notebooks; this trip was evidently to
be made with the noticeable absence of a legislative sidekick.

Doubtful weather conditions did not lessen Drew's resolve that they take off immediately. The continental
breakfast that Daran found before her swayed from side
to side as they reached their cruising altitude amid thick,

180

ominous clouds, high winds, and abominable air pockets. It was, in hindsight, the worst flight she had ever been on. Ironically it was just that discomfort that alleviated, then remedied the storm within her.

Sitting beside her, Drew could not miss the death-grip she held on the arms of her seat, her eyes wide and glued to the window and the nothingness beyond. "It's all right, Daran. You're not frightened, are you?" His voice had softened, miraculously, giving her the courage to look at him.

"I hate flying anyway. And in this type of weather . . ."

His gaze fell to the typed memoranda on his lap for a minute before he reinserted them in their manila folder and put them back into his briefcase. Shoving the arm between their seats back and out of the way, he took her hand, which hovered unsurely. "Come here." His head cocked enticingly, yet there was none of the sensuality in his eye that there might have been. "You'll feel better. Lean against me."

It had an instant calming effect, the steady beat of his heart beneath her ear and the firm clasp of his arm around her shoulder, holding her securely in defiance of the plane's sporadic bobbing. It was a peaceful haven, one which she needed badly. Between the comfort of the pose and her fatigue, she lost track of time. It was only when she darted a glance at her watch that she bolted upright.

"We've been in the air for more than two hours. Where is Bradley Field?" Had they been on course, they would have touched down long since.

Drew hesitated, a breath drawn, before he answered. "You're coming to Montreal with me."

It was a gently spoken statement, made with neither humor nor smugness. Yet it unleashed a well of emotion within her. "But I can't go to Montreal. I'm expected back

181

home. There are too many things I have to do." Every excuse was a lame one; Drew knew it as did she. In response he merely pulled her head back against the solid wall of his chest and held her tighter than ever.

"Please, Daran. Don't fight me all the time. I'm trying to do what is best." There was a pleading note in his voice that she had heard on only one or two occasions in the past. As it had then, now it affected her deeply. The strength of the man was unfathomable; even in that hint of vulnerability, it showed through. When he saw that she would not argue, he continued, gently stroking her hair, tucking each strand behind her ear.

"I have to attend some important meetings in Montreal. But they shouldn't take more than several hours on each of Saturday and Sunday. This is Friday; we have nearly the entire weekend to ourselves. *I* need this time, and *you* need this time. *We* do. Just trust me." Hypnotized by the soothing touch of his fingers on her face, she forgot even the intermittent buffeting of the airplane. "I made a promise to you that I would never hurt you. And I have every intention of holding to that promise. We are going to land soon. I have made arrangements for us to stay at the home of a friend of mine in the city. He is away now." When she tried to pull away in protest, he strengthened the hold of his arm. "No, don't run yet. If at the end of the weekend you want to return to Connecticut, I will take you back there with no questions asked. Fair enough?"

The old battle waged again. This time, however, the sides were grossly mismatched. While the small voice within told her to protest this compromising arrangement, the louder voice praised it. The soft laugh that came from Drew puzzled her. The hand at her head drew it back so that their eyes could meet. "I can feel the war this time, Daran. Don't worry. There are five bedrooms in this home, all available. You can have your choice. I won't bother you . . . if that's what you truly want."

If that's what you truly want. If that's what you truly want. The words gnawed at her all afternoon and evening. The drive through the city was an easy one, taking them directly to the address that Drew had given the French-speaking cabbie in passable French. The apartment itself was large and lovely. It didn't pass her notice that he put her bag in one room, his own in another. Biting her lip, she let it be.

It was as though Drew had decided to ignore her inner turmoil. He was the perfect gentleman, as he had been on so many of their earliest outings in Connecticut. The weather had cleared with his mood, and she could not help but relax. A long walk on the paths of Mount Royal soothed her even more, the view of the city from its peak being well worth the exertion. Daran knew that the ball was in her hands; she could run with it or pass. For the rest of that afternoon and through dinner at a small but charming restaurant, she held it, wavering, unsure, knowing that it represented much more than a mere weekend's field play.

When they finally returned to the apartment, Drew spent several hours studying the papers he'd brought, leaving Daran to sit with him, resting back against the sofa, letting the sight of the man before her and the soft music on the stereo lull her to drowsiness. Still she made no move when he led her to her room, then gently kissed her forehead with a soft good night before heading down the hall to his own room.

With the darkness came the undeniable realization that she was most definitely in love with him. As she lay in bed waiting, listening, wondering, pondering, daring to hope, she knew that it was time for her finally to make her move.

Rising slowly from her bed, she made her way into the hall and to the door of his room. The racing of her pulse was the only sound as she entered, the soft click of the door as it closed behind her its only follow-up. The pale moonlight cast its glimmer on the form propped up against the headboard of the huge bed. It made no sign of welcome, merely waited for her.

Doe-soft steps took her to the edge of the bed. There she stood in silence, gazing at the man she knew she loved, needing now some small sign that he wanted her. That he was bare to the waist and beyond was barely hidden by the light sheet bunched about his hips. When he drew the sheet back and slowly eased himself from the bed to stand before her, she didn't flinch. Only then did he speak.

"Are you sure, honey? *Really* sure?"

The thickness in her throat choked off sound and breath. Yet she nodded with a sense of conviction that answered his question conclusively. When he took her in his arms, she was home. The soft moan that slipped through her trembling lips was muffled against the fine mat of hair on his chest, and she held him with every ounce of her strength, willing those old fears to oblivion, wishing never to leave this spot. For long moments he held her quietly, soothing her with his mere presence, letting her slowly gain confidence. Then he drew back and lowered his head, his lips capturing hers with a tenderness so sweet she could have cried out again.

Long fingers slipped beneath the thin straps of her gauzy nightgown, letting them fall down her arms and the soft material float to her feet. The air that touched her body was instantly warmed by his hands, tracing with devastating gentleness the curves of her femininity he had only begun to imagine. When the quivering of her knees betrayed her emotions, he lifted her off her feet and laid her carefully on the bed, sitting down beside her to drink

184

in her beauty. The path his eyes took heated her blood, wrapping her in a cocoon of warmth and desire. Then he looked at her face once more, capturing her eyes as he had the awesome power to do. All other thought fled but that of the desperate love she felt.

"I don't want you to be frightened, Daran," he crooned softly, beginning to stroke her hair and her face before letting his hands drop to her shoulders, then to her breasts. "Please trust me. Let me love you." Whether the word had been merely a figure of speech, she no longer cared. She did trust him. Bill no longer existed, nor did the trauma he had inflicted on her on nights such as this, in the darkness, on his bed. Now there was only Drew and his magnificence—his body and his hands that stroked Daran to distraction.

Her own hands found their way to his chest, caressing its sinewed firmness, then moving to his waist and hips. With a moan, he lowered himself beside her, drawing her into his arms and against the full form of his masculinity. Kisses merged with caresses, then sparked an exploration of each other that fanned the raging fires. Their breath melded together in short gasps, their tongues sought solace in and on one another. No part of her was left untouched as she reached a height that only his full possession could exceed. At the moment she would have begged for release, he hesitated, studying her eyes a final time for a sign of that haunted shadow. Its absence was the sweetest victory he had ever tasted.

Never would she forget that moment, nor the one that followed as he took her, filling her with such mind-shattering ecstasy that she understood, for the first time, the full potential of her womanhood. Again and again he led her on that rapturous climb, forging higher and higher, reaching new and unimagined summits, joining her in the climactic and shuddering joy that left them both, at long last, spent but satisfied. When she slept, it was in his arms; when he slept, it was in hers. Neither permitted the other escape; neither wanted it. It was a night Daran would always cherish, a night when she lived the depth of a love she had never before felt or imagined. As she slept, she had no way of knowing that the waves of peace and fulfillment that surged silently through her came directly from the long, muscled male form curved intimately around her, itself awash with peace and fulfillment for the first time in many, many years.

CHAPTER 9

A gentle rain of kisses brought her eyes slowly open to face the dawn, just broken over the city, and the man beside her, his hands gently caressing her.

"Good morning," he drawled softly. "How did you sleep?"

As the memory of where she was, and the night that had just been, winged her into consciousness, she smiled. "Never better." Raising her face, she sought his lips with her own, thanking him wordlessly for the joy he had brought her, unknowing of the greater one to come.

It was a warm murmur against her lips. "I love you, Daran." Her amber gaze, fully alert suddenly, shot to the silken gray beam that took up the caress of his lips. "I've never said that to any woman. But I do love you, Daran. Is that so very hard to believe?" He had read the incredulity in her expression and challenged it quietly.

Several moments passed before thoughts formed coherently in her emotional whirlwind. "It's hard to believe that something you've felt and wanted for so long can actually be true."

The arms that tightened convulsively about her told of his own joy; the demand of his kiss spoke of his need for reassurance. When he finally let her speak, the words that had been held back would be no longer. "And *I* love *you.* I never thought I'd be able to tell you that, but it's true."

Daran's heart was racing as wildly as Drew's when he hauled her head back against his chest. "I love you, Drew," she whispered moments before the circle of his strong arms cut off her breath, only to relax an instant later in the resumption of the gentle exploration that so thrilled her. The trail of his hands blazed over her back, her hips, and her thighs, and they set fire to every point they touched before they turned to climb over her abdomen and rib cage to her breasts, now straining and full. With the knowledge of his love tucked into her heart, she opened herself to him as never before. But it was no passive offering, for her own desire was to touch and explore him with this newfound confidence. The strength of back, shoulders, and chest rippled beneath her questing fingers. The smoothness of his hips, the fine texture of his thighs, the rising ardor of his manhood—all gave her as much pleasure as his workings on her.

Soft words of love flew back and forth amid the torrent of emotions that engulfed them. If the night had been one of discovery, this early morning tryst was one of enhancement. Freed forever of the fears that had held her captive for so long, she gave of herself totally, with more passion than she had known she possessed. And it was matched by Drew's, so rich and deep and beautiful. Again they soared to mutually climactic heights. Again each new pulsing spiral surpassed the last in intensity.

The sun's first rays skittered on the window sill when they finally lay back to let the tremors subside. As she cuddled close beside him, their damp bodies in perfect and restful fit, she heard the words once more. "I love you." Whether it was her own voice, which had intoned the vow so soulfully, or his, did not matter. It was a mutual expression of what they had experienced.

Very slowly the heartbeat beneath her ear steadied. "I thought last night was magnificent, Daran," he murmured, half-dazed with exhaustion, "but this has topped even that." Again he spoke for them both, voicing the very thoughts that filtered through her own haze. But there were other thoughts, things she wanted desperately to tell him.

"You made it so beautiful for me, Drew," she began, lifting her head to rest her chin on his chest. "You were so gentle. I needed that." Eyes that had been closed now opened in gray anticipation of what was to come. "There was only one other man—"

"Shh." A strong hand seized her head and forced it around and back to its more restful pose.

"But I want you to know—"

"I don't *want* to know." The softness of his tone carried its force nonetheless. "I love you now. The past isn't important. It's the future that matters to us. God, how I love you!" It was as though he could not say it enough. The fierceness of his hug drove all though of that past from her mind. He was right; it was their love that mattered now.

Within minutes the steady rhythm of his breathing turned to the slow rhythm of sleep. Content and fulfilled, Daran lay with him, reveling in his peacefulness though wide awake herself. Her eye followed the lines of his body, bare and gleaming in the growing light. He was all man. That she had known for months. Yet, now, as she unabashedly thrilled at the sight of him, she knew even more. For his lovemaking had been masterful, his virility exquisite. It was all she could do to keep from reaching out and touching him again, from awakening him, from guiding him once more to her. The familiar tingling erupted in her loins. Wishing to still it, yet refusing to remove herself from the intimate circle of his body, she forced her mind to other thoughts.

But there were none to be found. All thoughts at that moment revolved around Drew. And the future. What would it hold? If he loved her as she did him, could they make it work? It was the same quandary that had been present so often in her mind. Politics was a marriage unto itself; it was, in its way, all-consuming. Yet the past few months had shown her what one man, a politician at that, could do if he so wished. Drew had made the time for her. During those hectic weekends in Connecticut, he had always made time for something personal in each day. Even in Washington, where his demeanor had been much more formal, he had shown that, when he wished, he could find the time to spend with her, whether in the Capitol corridors, in his office, at her hotel suite, in his condominium, or at a restaurant. If he wished, he could find the time.

Her mother's words returned to her, and the lesson was there. It was one thing to plan a life with Drew, another to anticipate one without him. The latter was total anathema to her. She loved Drew. And, yes, she was willing to make sacrifices, to make changes in her personal life to accommodate his. Surely there could be found a happy solution. There were excellent colleges in Washington where she might possibly find a position. The point was to be with him, to be there when he was, where he was. If they loved each other, all things would find proper places in their lives.

On that optimistic note she finally drifted into a deep and dreamless sleep. When a voice came suddenly, loud and alert, to her ear, she jumped. "What is it, Drew?"

The room was bright in morning sun. "Damn it! My watch—where did I put it! I hardly ever take it off—"

"The dresser," she interrupted softly, lying back with a smug grin on the bed, pulling the sheet to her chest as she watched the lithe figure bound across the room. *He was magnificent!* And, she beamed with satisfaction, he had taken off his wristwatch for her. That he had done that—a man who was positively addicted to the passing of the second hand—was a tribute unto itself. For he had known, last night, that she would come to his room; as surely as he had known how to woo her, he had expected her.

"And what is so funny?" The growl was a playful one, offered as the tall form turned back to her, strapping on his watch, then coming to stand, in all his natural majesty, by the bed.

The flush on her cheeks was unmistakably a love-blush. "Not funny," she corrected gently, "but lovely. You are. Your body is." Her gaze ran the length of it before returning to his eyes. "But, there *is* one thing I still don't understand about it." The smile that played on her lips spoke of mischief.

The mattress yielded beneath his weight as Drew sat down beside her. A tawny eyebrow returned the mischievous slant, arching beneath the hair that fell carelessly across his forehead. "Now what could that be? As I recall it, you were pretty . . . thorough earlier today."

She was to be neither embarrassed nor discouraged from asking the question. "How do you keep that tan, busy as you are?" Her hand reached to trace the distinct line where bronze ended and pallor began, low on his abdomen. "It can't be all from the pool in Simsbury; you're never there." Drew sucked in his breath as she spoke, then grabbed her hand in mock punishment.

"Keep on doing that, honey, and you'll never make it there either. I may just keep you in bed round the clock." His expression sobered as he paused, seeming to hold his breath for the moment. "You *are* going to marry me, aren't you, Daran?"

The whispered words of love that had been spoken before had made no mention of marriage. But the idea had been there, in Daran's mind, for weeks. Even with the few lingering doubts, she could not deny either him or herself.

"Yes." It was as simply said as that.

A broad grin, the whitest ever in that famous smile, cut through the lean hollows of his cheeks. "Then you'd sure as hell better learn to control those wandering fingers of yours and let your intended get shaved, showered, and dressed. Otherwise he's apt to be out of a job."

Eyes widened, she stared at him. "Your appointment—what time was it for?"

With deliberate nonchalance, he glanced at his watch. "They are expecting me in five minutes."

"Five minutes? You'll be late—"

The weight of his body fell across hers, one hand snaking out to grab the phone. Within minutes he had bought an additional half-hour. Then, with a pat to her bottom perfectly outlined beneath the smoothness of the sheet, he headed for the bathroom.

It was an experience of sheer delight to stand, wrapped togalike in that same sheet, at the bathroom door and watch the man at work. The towel around his hips, so slim as his body tapered from the breadth of his shoulders, was a merciful diversion without which she feared for her sanity. They talked softly as he shaved, then more loudly through the steady beat of the shower, then not at all when he whipped the sheet from her and hauled her into the torrent with him. It was a dangerous game, he told her tongue-in-cheek and hands about her waist, but neither shied from it. Fortunately the water turned cold in time to prevent Drew from having to make another call for time.

The weekend passed as in a dream, a perfect honeymoon before the fact. As Drew had predicted, his meetings took up no more than several hours of each of the days. During that time Daran explored and admired the maze of underground shopping malls for which Montreal was famous, though she was ever grateful to reemerge into the sunshine and await Drew's return.

The streets of the city passed beneath their feet as they strolled, arm in arm, up one and down the next. From Drew's viewpoint, half of the luxury was in the anonymity that the strange city and its country afforded. From Daran's, it was his company, and his alone, which was the luxury.

A horsedrawn buggy carted them through the oldest section of the city, over cobblestone streets and past ancient landmarks. The extensive and efficient metro system delivered them to Olympic Park, where they viewed the swimming complex and its five pools, the velodrome and its helmut-shaped roof, and the stadium, where the Expos led the Yankees by a score of 10 to 3 at the bottom of the eighth.

They ambled through the parks, scattered about the city, talking of politics and love, academia and love, and then, marriage. By mutual agreement their wedding would be a private affair, taking place after the Senate adjourned for the year, thereby allowing them the sufficiently long honeymoon that Drew felt they both deserved. And, at his insistence, Labor Day would see them both in Cleveland to spend several days with her family.

There was but one blemish on the full run of her happiness. Drew did not yet know of her prior marriage, short and disastrous as it had been. He did not yet know about Bill Longley. Several times after that initial attempt she broached the subject; each time, he declared firmly that he did not want to hear, that he did not want her to recall that very painful experience again. In his mind the trauma had been a one-time physical ordeal; he knew nothing of her own folly in having married Bill, or that her former husband had gone on to become a member of the House of Representatives, or that it had been that very man whose appearance had so distressed her in the restaurant in Washington that last night.

The truth would have to come out before that trip to Ohio; of that Daran was certain. Her sureness did not extend, however, to the best way of divulging it. And her happiness in Drew's presence was so great that she willingly let this one matter fall to the wayside for the time being.

Wearing the elegant aqua silk she had purchased in Washington a mere few days before—never imagining then that she would be wearing it under these circumstances—she accompanied Drew on Saturday night to an equally as elegant French restaurant in the old quarter of the city. Stained-glass windows were lit by the gaslights on the street outside; fine linen, china, and silver lay on the table before them. They were treated like royalty, with Drew's anonymity intact. A gourmet's delight, the fare was authentic and delicious, as was the wine they sipped, their eyes meeting in quiet communication throughout. Their lovemaking later that evening reflected the growth of their love in that one day alone. And it left Daran praying that the weekend would never end. For, despite those vows of love, there was still the world to face and, with it, the oft-times problematic twist of reality.

Once cynical about the brotherhood of politics as a whole, now she saw that error. For Drew was none of the things that Bill, and so many of the others she'd met in Ohio, represented. He was proud yet sensitive, demanding yet giving, practical yet honest, strong yet gentle. The months in which she'd come to know Drew Charles had quickly cured her of her own arrogant generalization. Yet there was another factor, one which continued to frighten her.

To be in love, on their own, in a faraway place, was one thing. To be in love amid a battalion of aides and colleagues, contributors and constituents, lobbyists, the press, and the public eye itself was entirely different. Would their love be strong enough to withstand the grueling late-night sessions, the interminable evening meetings, the frequent separations? Would their love be strong enough to counter the negative elements which might contribute to their alienation from one another? Legislative aides had been known to pull rank over wives in the past; would she fall victim to this? These were all worries of the future that only the future would resolve. For the first time in her life, however, she believed in true love and its power to succeed in taming, in this case, the political machine. Her love was so great that it was worth a try.

It was late Sunday evening when their plane touched down at Bradley Field to deposit Daran, then take Drew on to Washington. It had been agreed that he would return home the following weekend, and that, for the time being, they would say nothing of their plans, if for no other reason than to savor their own privacy a little longer. His kiss was long and hard, with a fervor to last the week, as they stood for those last few moments by the plane together. He, too, sensed the test to come. For, once back in Washington, he was the senator, subject to the very demanding forces that had wrecked many a home. Once he had sworn never to ask a woman to share his kind of life. Now he had repudiated that pledge. Within the endless power play of the political arena, there would be forces working against them daily. He could not forget that any more than he could forget the last miserable years of his mother's life. Yes, he, too, had his doubts, but he also knew the strength of the love he felt for Daran. It *was* worth a try.

Each night she waited for his call. Each night it came.

It was the highlight of her existence. For, though she found herself involved in meetings or on the phone with one thing or another, supposed vacation time notwithstanding, her thoughts rarely strayed from her love and her lover.

When she met him at the airport on Friday evening, she had never been happier. Tired as he was, Drew shared the sentiment. And though there were the usual appearances to be made during the weekend, they found time to be together, to talk, to love. The patience with which he discussed his work, outlining in particular the pressure he was under on the nomination of Rudolph Sweet to the Supreme Court, pleased her, indicative as it was of the sharing that would characterize their married life.

"My distinguished colleagues—" his frustration unleashed itself in part in the exaggerated drawl of the term "—have been on my back, pushing me to take a stand. But it's not as easy as it sounds, and this confirmation could hinge on a handful of us. I want to be sure of my decision. It's a controversial appointment."

The night was warm and sultry, as late summer nights in the Connecticut Valley tended to be. From Daran's house, where Drew was staying, they had followed the trail through the woods to his for an evening swim. Now they lay, talking, side by side on the large patio chaise. "Why the controversy?" she asked softly.

"The man had an alcohol problem over twenty years ago. There was an automobile accident in which his wife was crippled. He was drunk and slightly hurt himself, but there are those who still feel that he could have gotten help sooner. Since the accident he has been a practicing attorney, accepting cases that many an other would have rejected. It's a penance of sorts. Five years ago he was named to the bench in Toledo. His record is spotless."

"No more drinking?"

"Not since the accident. His wife is an invalid. He has pampered her devotedly ever since."

In a totally absent-minded gesture she rubbed her cheek against the texture of his chest. "I don't see what the problem is then. If his qualifications are there, what stands in the way of confirmation?"

A kind and indulgent chuckle hovered by her ear. "You make it all sound so simple. Unfortunately he does have a past." *Don't we all,* she mused ruefully; as yet, she had not found the right time to tell him of Bill. "As a justice of the United States Supreme Court, he will pass judgment on many sensitive issues. His opinions will affect many people. Ironically, had it not been for a small and vocal group that opposes the nomination, the past might have been long forgotten, where I believe it should be. The issue, now, however, is whether he can be accepted as a symbol of lawfulness, a figure of authority. It boils down to the legitimacy of our government." He paused, clearing his throat uncomfortably. "Then, there is the usual politicking. You know, this one wants an Easterner in the seat, and that one wants a woman—"

"Most of which has little to do with the merits of that man who was nominated!"

"Touché!" His arms tightened in playful diversion. Suddenly this talk of Washington palled. What he really wanted at that moment was to make love to his woman, here, on the patio, beneath the moonlight. Which he promptly did.

For Daran, it seemed too good to be true. The end of the weekend found her, if possible, more in love than before. Parting on Sunday was the hardest of all, despite the knowledge that the following Thursday would see them together again and for the entire length of the holiday recess.

The odd premonition that gripped her had no basis in fact. Perhaps it was superstition; things were simply flowing too smoothly to be believed. Perhaps it was merely a reluctance to be away from him, even for those few days. Whatever, it disquieted her. In some odd way it was no surprise to find Stanley Morrow at the door of her hospital office the next morning, shortly before noon.

"Have you seen the papers, Daran?" he exclaimed loudly, his voice a mixture of anger and bewilderment. During the time that she and Drew had spent together in the state, she had come to know Stan Morrow well. Though the formalities of Mr. and Dr. had been dropped, the two got along only on a marginal basis. As had been her very first impression of the man, she found him far too pushy for her taste, though it was this trait that made him so valuable to Drew. Now she was perplexed.

"What papers?" Sleep had been slow in coming last night. In compensation she had arisen later than usual, having to forego her usual coffee and newspaper in her efforts to get to the hospital on time. Her two morning appointments had ended; now there was simply paper work to clean up.

"The *Washington Post,* for one. The *Hartford Courant,* for another. Take your pick. The *Bridgeport Post.* The *New Haven Register.* The *Waterbury American.* They've all got it!" For a man customarily in full control, at least outwardly, he had hit rock bottom. His hands gestured wildly, his eyes bore a frantic glint.

"Got what?" His mood was contagious, translating to fear in Daran as visions flitted before her.

With a sigh of exasperation he shoved the first of the papers at her. Her hand accepted it gingerly, her feet took her back to her chair behind the desk. Without further word Stanley Morrow entered the room and closed the door behind him.

Instant shock registered as the amber eyes perused first one, then the other papers. Worded differently, the headlines were substantively the same. CHARLES SCANDAL ERUPTS; SWEET HEARINGS HALTED. CHARGES OF BRIBERY ON SWEET CONFIRMATION CENTER ON SENATOR ANDREW CHARLES. CHARLES OF CONNECTICUT IS PAID TO SUPPORT SWEET NOMINATION. To her horror, they got worse. CHARLES SELLS OUT FOR LATEST WOMAN. THE INCORRUPTIBLE CHARLES TAKES FALL ON SWEET ISSUE.

"What is this all about, Stan?" she cried incredulously.

"I was hoping you could tell me that." With the calming of his initial uproar, hardness had set into his voice, as it had into his eyes. "Read on."

Mind whipping in every direction at once, she could not. "You tell me what they say. I can't read them. *What is this all about?*"

There was undue skepticism in his study of her, undue sarcasm in his voice. "It seems that you have been paid on the side to woo Drew into supporting the nomination of Rudolph Sweet to the Supreme Court."

Brows knit in puzzlement, face contorted in disbelief, she sat back in her chair. "*What?*"

Calmly, with accusation written clearly between the lines, he went on. "It seems that you are being paid by a Representative William Longley from Toledo, Ohio, who coincidentally is sponsoring the nomination personally in the House. Having wormed your way into the senator's good graces on another issue, you are now pushing this one. Of course the bribery is not in the form of money to the senator himself. He has no need of that. Rather, it is in the form of favors." He had saved the best for last. Opening a tabloid with deliberate slowness, he spread it on the desk before her. There, blown up in black and white,

199

were pictures of the two of them, locked in each other's arms, first at the airport the night he had dropped her back from Montreal, then at her front door—*her own front door*—this past weekend.

"How did they ever get these—" Her whisper of astonishment barely reached his ears.

"That's not the point!" The roar that hit her sat her up straight in her chair. "The point is that this scandal could ruin Drew, after all he's worked for. Why on earth did you do it? Were you that badly in need of money?"

From the maelstrom of her thoughts came the word *money*. Bill Longley. Money. Regular payments. "Oh, my God!" A trembling hand flew to her lips as the depth of the misunderstanding hit her. Was it misunderstanding—or purposeful malice? Who could have done this—planted such a story in all these papers? Surely not Bill, for his own name would necessarily be soiled. Any jealousy he had felt, if there had been any that night, seeing her in the restaurant with another man, would have been expressed in a very different way, if she knew anything about Bill Longley. But *this*—what was *this* all about?

Aside from the things that remained to be deciphered, one course of action was obvious and urgent. Drew had to be told the truth as soon as possible. Gaining strength with the decision, she looked up at the glowering face of his Hartford office head. "Would you excuse me, Stan. I have to get in touch with Drew."

The near sinister grin that spread over Stan's lips sent a chill through her. "I'm sure that's what you would like to do. Good luck." Without another word he left. In his wake she began to tremble uncontrollably, wondering exactly what he meant. It did not take her long to find out. Three times within the next fifteen minutes she tried to get through to Drew. The first time, John put her off, claiming that he was on another line. The second time, Leo did the chore, elaborating on an important meeting that he was headed for in the Caucus Room. In both cases their tones of voice had been cool and even. On impulse she spoke with the receptionist the third time, only to be told that Drew was channeling all calls through either Leo or John.

An hour later she tried again. The results were the same. As she had done earlier, she left word for him to call her. Then she sat and waited, then paced the floor. In desperation she left the hospital and drove home, dialing the number of his office immediately on her arrival. This time the receptionist was less patient. "Dr. Patterson, your message is here and waiting. The senator will get back to you as soon as possible. He is very busy today." It could as easily have been a recording, a far cry from the young woman Daran remembered as being so friendly. Something was wrong—and it had everything to do with those articles. Leaving a revised message as to her whereabouts, she hung up the phone, then began the wait anew.

At first it was merely suspicion, wild and dreadful, based, she told herself, on pure imagination. Of course Drew would return her call. He loved her. Hadn't he told her that just yesterday?

Yet, as the hours passed, she became less convinced. She knew his schedule, as did the other aides. He was in and out all the time; no one meeting or appointment ever lasted more than half an hour, save those more binding committee hearings and, of course, the Senate floor debates and votes. Had he wanted to return her call, he would have already done so. Or sent word through one of the others as to when he might. But nothing—nothing had come through on her silent phone.

When, by late afternoon, there was no sign of contact, she tried once more, one final time. Heart heavy, the receiver was as lead in her hand, falling instantly upon transmitting the news that the senator had left his office

201

for the day. Blinded by the tears that flowed uncontrollably, she wandered around the house, stunned, hurt, aching for the love which had been, poignantly and with lightning speed, sabotaged.

There seemed but one thing to do. Suitcases that had but barely been put away were now opened and filled once more. The clothes she had worn that morning to the hospital would do for the trip. Pure habit directed her from Simsbury to the airport, where she parked her car and headed for the ticket counter. Suddenly the choice faced her. Cleveland had been her original destination. But the flight to Washington left in twenty minutes; she could be on it as easily. Then she recalled the chilling tones of the Stans, the Leos, the Johns of the political world, and she knew that she could not bear to hear that same icy note from Drew. Heartbroken, she headed for Cleveland.

CHAPTER 10

Mary Abbott had been an angel, sending her devoted Hugh off by himself while she attempted to soothe her distraught daughter. With infinite patience and understanding, she listened as the story unfolded, from the very first meeting nearly four months ago in that tiny office at Trinity to the glare of the newspaper headlines the day before. In a way she had not done for years, she held Daran while she cried, soulfully and mournfully, until the tears were finally spent. Then, in the wee hours of the morning, they worked together to try to understand what had happened.

None of it made sense. It seemed such a simple misunderstanding, that to have been turned into something as odious as it had been was ludicrous. For some unfathomable reason, someone had dug into Daran's past, twisted the facts dramatically, and thereby set off a chain reaction. There were the obvious whos and whys. What bothered her most, however, was Drew. What had become of his love for her, if its basic trust could not survive a test such as this?

Exhaustion took its toll at dawn, drawing Daran into a restless sleep from which she awoke, several hours later, as miserable as ever. The only gratification was her mother's tireless presence, the best friends she had always hoped that one day they might be. For everything Daran might have resented in her childhood, Mary Abbott came through for her now.

Yet all of their searching left them lost. Drew *had* to have known of the falsehood of the newspaper reports. He had always, and would always, make his own decisions; even the most ambitious of his aides knew that. Could it be possible that he suspected she may have intended to do something, when her outspokenness had first goaded him into seeking her out? Again it boiled down to that matter of trust.

As the day wore on and Mary and Hugh prepared to go to a dinner at the Club, Daran was left to her own brooding. With the wearing off of the initial shock and a faint dulling of the excruciating pain she had felt earlier, two things became clearer.

The first was that what had happened, as sketchily as she could outline it, had been very much what she had feared. Once before she had been singed by the political fire. Even given the differences, monumental as they were, between Bill and Drew, the surrounding forces were the same. Hadn't she been skeptical of the unqualified happiness she and Drew had temporarily found? Hadn't she had a premonition?

The second was the nagging thought that, by running as she had to Cleveland, she had shown some guilt. What *had* prompted her to bypass that Washington shuttle to head to Ohio? The answer was not a hard one for a counselor, trained as she was, to discover. Loneliness. Thought of being without Drew, of having him taken from her so crassly, created such a pit of loneliness and despair that it had been an instinctive urge to return home, to the womb, as it were. Then it had seemed the only course. Now she wondered.

"Are you sure you won't come with us, dear?" Her mother stood at the door to kitchen, where Daran sat, alone, curled on a low window seat. "The Foxes will be here very soon, but you could still change and come. They'd all love to see you." There was a hint of mother coaxing child, as had been Mary's wont, in the words, a luring lilt in the tone. A pitiful semblance of a smile was Daran's only response to the memory.

"No, Mother. You go ahead. You've been wonderful to sit with me like this all day."

Her mother walked farther into the room to stand by Daran. "There has to be some explanation, Daran. I know what you think of us political creatures, but you are one too. And you always have a rational explanation for everything you do."

Sarcasm edged Daran's words. "Rational is one thing; appropriate is another. I think I may have blown it, flying out here as soon as the fur began to fly. But—" her amber eyes looked beseechingly up at her mother's kind face "—why didn't he return my calls?"

"What calls? I never *got* any calls!" The sound of the deep voice, agitated and weary, brought both heads, mother's and daughter's, to the door.

Daran bolted from her seat. "Drew!" It was a whispered exclamation of disbelief at this latest turn. Frozen to where she stood, she merely stared at the vision at the door. He was tired, though properly groomed, as she would have expected. Age seemed to have etched another five years on his features since she had seen him two days ago. The lines around his eyes and his mouth were more distinct, the tension gripping the bridge of his nose unmistakable. The strides that brought him into the kitchen and toward the two women were measured tautly.

"Mrs. Abbott, I'm Drew Charles." His introduction was formal, as was the hand that reached to clasp hers for a minute. The clenching of his jaw told of his attempt at restraint. So he *had* believed at least part of that malicious gossip!

The pain that shot through Daran's chest nearly robbed her of her breath. His fury was in check, but nonetheless real. As tears gathered at the backs of her eyes, the urge to flee gripped her once more. She darted toward the door, only to be stopped short by the force of a steel clamp on her arm.

"You wait for me!" he seethed, the gray of his eyes cold and merciless. Then the expression grew milder as he turned to Mary Abbott. "Daran will be returning to Washington with me as soon as she can get her things together. She has a lot of explaining to do for this little stunt!"

Then, as she had so gratifyingly done during the last day, Mary Abbott came to Daran's aid. "Now just a minute, Senator. This is *my* daughter, and I think you'd better begin by taking your hand off her. You're hurting her." Later Daran would be able to laugh at the spirit her mother had shown. Now, however, she was only thankful that the hand slowly slipped from her arm. So engrossed was she in a massage of the bruised area that she missed the hint of a smile that twitched at the corners of Drew's mouth.

"Thank you." Her mother went on, chin lifted by her momentary sense of power. "Now perhaps you would tell me exactly what you have in mind for my daughter?"

Though somber, Drew's anger had waned. For a long moment he turned to stare at Daran, his gaze as unfathomable as the ocean depth. Then he addressed her mother. "I'll be more than happy to do that while your daughter packs. A plane is waiting, not to mention the taxi outside."

Daran had no intention of going anywhere with Drew, considering his mood. But she was more than glad, at that moment, to escape the room. The sight of such fury directed at her by the man she loved to distraction was more than she could bear. Within minutes she had taken refuge in the sunporch at the other end of the house, where she sank into a corner hammock and hugged her stomach protectively. She did not even have the strength to ponder the content of the discussion going on in the other room. A gasp of mixed emotions slipped through her lips as the slam of a car door and the turn of an engine filtered across the yard, through the trees, and into the private screened enclosure in which she sat huddled in misery. So he had left . . .

"Okay, Daran. Let's go!" He hadn't left. That must have been her parents leaving—deserting her. What next?

Slowly she shook her head. "I'm not going back to Washington, Drew. I didn't want to go there in the first place. It was a mistake. I knew it would be. You talked me into it then," she spat out in weak accusation, "but you won't do it now."

Fully believing her, he took a different approach. Without a word, he left the porch, going back into the house. Within minutes he returned, her suitcase and purse in one hand, grabbing her arm with the other. "Let's go. You can change on the plane."

Her protest was fully expected and met by the same steel front. "Look, I've never abused a woman, and I don't intend to begin now," he growled, half-dragging her to the door. "Your mother will be calling you tomorrow morning in Washington. I gave her the number of my condominium. Now let's get a move on. The pilot is waiting."

"I'm not going to your condominium!"

With deafening thunder, both of voice and eye, he turned on her, towering ominously. "Shut up, Daran! So help me, you've pushed me to the limit. Now keep still!"

It was not so much fear as a sudden lethargy that sapped her strength to resist. The ride to the airport was

207

a silent one. Eyes glued to the window, she avoided those that studied her so closely, drawing prickles at the back of her neck with their intensity. Once aboard the airplane, she changed into a skirt and blouse, donned high heels and make-up, tugged her hair mercilessly into a tight bun away from her face, and resumed the identity of Dr. Daran Patterson, child psychologist. There was an impersonality about her professional side which suited her now, though whether the tentative shell of composure that accompanied it would last long, she wasn't sure. Throughout the flight Drew sat before her, excusing himself only for intermittent breaks to use the telephone in the cockpit.

"I can't go anywhere," she snapped sarcastically, when the gray gaze became an irritant. But he merely continued to stare at her, searching and punishing in turn.

The evening hour saw her ushered into Drew's office, where, to her chagrin, the three people with whom she had spoken briefly and abortively on the phone the day before sat, suddenly more alert with her appearance.

"Thank you for coming over," Drew greeted them, firmly escorting Daran to a seat by the window, farther from the others than the desk, behind which he now took refuge. "There's something that has to be clarified. And I'd like to do it now." The others nodded their heads as though there had been some choice in the matter; in fact, they either had to show up or they would have been shipped out in the morning. Daran waited, apprehension gnawing at her insides much as the gypsy moth caterpillars had gnawed at the huge maples beyond her Simsbury door last spring. Was she to be confronted on her part in the alleged bribery scheme before these others? Willing a poise she far from felt, she crossed one knee over the other, smoothed her skirt, and calmly folded her hands in her lap. With a sharp look in her direction to assure her attention, Drew began.

"John, I understand that Daran called me yesterday. Did you take that call?"

For the first time since she had known John Hollings, he squirmed. "It was absolutely a madhouse here yesterday, Drew. There were so many calls—"

The gray eyes narrowed. "Did she call?"

"Yes."

"And why wasn't she put through to me?" His voice held a challenge that his administrative assistant was fast to meet.

"You were on the phone or out of the office most of the day yourself."

The line of Drew's chin squared in anger. "Why didn't I receive any message that she called?"

"Come on, Drew. She was the last one you wanted to hear from—"

The tall man rose from behind his desk, fists clenched, voice booming. "*And who told you that?*" Then, as quickly, he gained control of himself. In the instant his torrid gaze passed to the next face, that of Leo Alteris. "Did *you* speak with Daran at any point yesterday?"

Leo glanced quickly at John for encouragement but found none. "Yes. She, ah, called several times. I thought I left a message. Perhaps, in the uproar, it was misplaced . . ."

At that moment, Daran could have spit. It was bad enough that Drew was verifying her own claims before these people. For an instant, she recalled the time, several weeks after she had arrived in Connecticut, when the teller at the bank had refused, in a voice loud enough to be heard by the line of people behind her, to honor her out-of-state check. This, however, was even more humiliating. And to hear John, then Leo . . . *misplaced, hah!*

"Perhaps . . ." was Drew's murmured echo as he turned to the last of the trio, the petite receptionist. "And what

209

about you, Cindy? Do you recall speaking with Daran yesterday?"

Of the three, the girl was the only one with the courtesy to lower her head in token remorse. "Yes. I took down her number, but . . ."

". . . but never gave it to me?" he prodded, his voice low and steady. When the young girl shook her head, Drew pulled himself up to a greater height. "Thank you. You've answered my questions perfectly. I only wish I hadn't had to ask them. Now—" He lowered his own head and took a deep breath, turning his back on the group to face his desk. In profile as Daran saw him, there was a sense of defeat written over his features. "If you'll excuse us, I'd like to speak with Daran alone. John, please wait for a minute." Only when he heard the door close quietly behind the other two did he turn, his face a rigid mask of composure. Hands thrust in his pockets, she could not see their tension.

"This is far from over, John. You know that. I've never been as disappointed in my staff before. But we'll discuss that more tomorrow. I'd like you to go out there now and set up a press conference for—" he checked his watch "—an hour from now, at ten o'clock. I'll have a statement to make at that time."

John shook his head in doubt. "I'm not sure if they will appreciate the sudden—"

"I don't really give a damn about the press. Do it! If they don't like it, that's their problem. They don't have to come, if they want to risk missing the story." Cynicism was something she had never heard before in his tone; the eyes that had not strayed from his face for more than an instant in the last half hour now widened. As the boom of his voice slowly dissipated, John Hollings made his fast exit. Only then did Daran look away, suddenly fearful of what was to come next.

A deep silence penetrated the room for long moments before he spoke. "You're very quiet. Have you nothing to say for yourself?" The voice was rich yet sober, soft yet demanding. Daran's was a weak offering by comparison.

"What is there for me to say? I have so little idea of what's going on here or why, or what you want from me, for that matter." When she dared to lift her eyes, the ones which speared her from his perch on the edge of the desk constricted her breathing. His distrust, his disdain was made even worse by the pity now etched in his expression.

His voice was drained of all anger when he spoke. "Tell me what you are thinking, Daran." It was a command, for all its soft intonation. For what seemed an eternity, she debated ignoring it, fearing that to obey would be to magnify the misery, the humiliation, the pain she felt already. But the eyes that had locked into hers gave silent threat. Slowly she began.

"I'm thinking of all the things I should have told you weeks ago, things about my past I couldn't quite face myself." On the verge of divulging what none but her parents knew, she wavered.

"Go on." The voice that urged her to continue was marked with patience. Tearing her eyes from his, she stood, walked to the window, and stared out at the lights of the city beyond.

She cleared her throat and swallowed. "I was married, once, nearly six years ago. It was a disaster—six months of misery. His name was Bill Longley. He was from Ohio also. We met at a fund-raiser; my parents went to many and I often went with them. Bill and I dated for years. The night of my wedding I discovered that I was married to ... to ... ah, it doesn't matter. We were divorced after those six months; he has been paying alimony ever since. The money goes into my bank account every month; I have never touched it!" Whirling around, her eyes begged

211

that he believe her. "He went on, three years ago, to win a seat in the House of Representatives. I hadn't seen him since the divorce until that night, after the bill passed the floor vote, when we went out to celebrate . . ." Her voice trailed off and she sought silence for the split second it took her to realize that there was still more to be said.

"I *never, never* had any part in a scheme to influence you!" Her words fell against the top of the sandy head, bowed now, hiding his expression. But her own ire had been piqued. "I didn't want to have anything to do with you to begin with. Life in the political arena with Bill, even though it was all local in Ohio, was brutal enough. When I fell in love with you, I thought that maybe, together, we could buck the system. I was wrong, wasn't I?" She was trembling now as she faced him, being swept by the minute deeper into the vortex of her own torment.

"I was naive and stupid! But I never expected you to believe that story! How could you have thought that I was capable of doing something like that?" Her screams were abruptly cut off by the startled expression on his face when he lifted it to her gaze. But the fire of emotion, in full flame now, drove her on once more. "I thought you loved me! In my book that implies some basic trust. You chose to believe that shoddy journalistic—"

This time, her words were cut off by the hands that seized her arms and shook her. "Wait a minute, now! I never believed that story! I spent all of yesterday chasing down the source of that ugly piece, and she will have her day in court. But I never, for one minute, believed those allegations. And, speaking of trust, how great was yours in me, for you to pick up and run all the way to Cleveland without even speaking to me? Where was your trust? You said that you loved me, yet at its first test, you doubted me. How do you think that makes me feel? I've been around;

I knew what we'd be facing if we married. But I wanted to give it a shot . . ."

As his eyes blazed into hers, Daran's composure snapped. His own hurt, its very presence a rude awakening, told her how very wrong she'd been. Lifting her hands to cover her eyes, she burst into tears.

For long moments she was aware of nothing save the sorrow that flooded her and the steel grip that steadied her. Then, finally, she was hauled against Drew's chest and enfolded in that cocoon that offered its unique brand of protection. "God, Daran, please don't do this to yourself. We've both been wrong. I should have let you tell me about Bill before. You did try, but something in me wanted to believe that I was the first man to ever really mean something to you."

"You were!" Her eyes sought his through her tears, her words short and spoken in gasps. "I never loved Bill. Our marriage just . . . happened. It went on. There was no sharing, no giving, neither trust nor respect. And, as for sex, I suffered for days after each assault. I never even knew what an orgasm was . . . until we made love." Thoughts of the beauty of that night in Montreal brought a resumption of her tears. Again he hugged her to him, rocking her gently.

"Shh, shh. It's all right," he crooned. "Everything is going to be all right now."

Her voice was muffled against his shirt. "Is it? I don't think it's ever going to be all right. They'll always be there. If it isn't one, it will be another. There will always be someone or something there to ruin it—"

"We won't let that happen!" The commanding tone of the words by her ear made her want to believe it with all her heart. He was, once more, so sure, so confident, so much in control. "If you still love me as much as I love you, we can fight it!" This time his large hands framed her face, tilting it up toward his. "Do you love me?"

"Oh, Drew, I do!" Hers was a hoarse declaration, broken by lingering sobs, now of happiness and hope. "Do you really think we can do it?"

At last his smile settled on her, helping to erase her skepticism. "I know we can. You trusted me enough once before to open up a new world for you. Can you do it again?"

As she smiled his thumbs wiped away the last of her tears. "I can try." Her dark brows lifted in unknowing seductiveness.

The hands that had caressed her cheeks now slipped down to her waist, molding her closer to him. With a mischievous smile, he shook his head. "Sorry, not good enough. Trying is for politics; it's the only way we can phrase our campaign pledges without getting into too much trouble. Loving involves doing, not trying. Well?" He raised an eyebrow expectantly. "Can you trust me to love you for the rest of our lives?"

The adoration alight in her face was warm in her touch as her hands crept to the broad column of his neck. "Yes, Drew. I trust you now . . . in everything." The exertion of pressure in her fingers brought his head down for a kiss to seal her pledge. His own was whispered against the sweetness of her lips.

"I will love you always. And that, my dear Dr. Patterson, is a promise."

Fifteen minutes later, the members of the press corps were already gathered in Drew's office where he led Daran to a seat, then took his own behind his desk and within arm's reach of her. Their image of mutual composure was miraculous in light of their earlier emotional states. But they were both, now, committed to the limelight and they bore its demands well.

"Ladies and gentlemen," Drew began, speaking without papers or notes before him, "I thank you for coming on such short notice and at this late hour. I'm sure you will, however, understand the urgency of this matter. And I will try to be brief." A low-murmured wave of humor spread through the group at Drew's unspoken reference to his long-winded colleagues. "To my right—" he turned slightly and cast her a gentle glance "—is Dr. Daran Patterson. As a child psychologist well respected in her field, she has worked for the past four months as a member of my staff, helping to shape the Rights of Minors Act which the Senate has recently approved. There have been some unfortunate allegations made that Dr. Patterson has attempted to compromise me in respect to the judicial nomination of Rudolph Sweet. I would right now like to deny all such allegations as utterly false and malicious. At no time in our acquaintance has Daran Patterson ever attempted such a thing, nor would it have possibly succeeded had she done so. I believe she knows, as do those of you who have followed my career, that I speak my own mind.

"There were allegations," he went on succinctly, "that Dr. Patterson has been receiving money on a regular basis from a member of the House of Representatives, William Longley of Ohio. This claim is true. For a short period of time five years ago, the then State Senator Longley and Dr. Patterson were married. The payments she receives are alimony payments, as the court records will corroborate." The bent heads of the journalists focused on their notes while Drew focused on his thoughts, and Daran on her hands which had begun to tremble in spite of herself. As though sensing this, with all he had on his mind, Drew still reached over to squeeze a hand for a brief moment,

215

his eyes reminding her of her promise to him moments before. "I might add at this point," he continued, looking at her a second longer before facing front again, "that those payments will end before the New Year. Daran and I hope to be married as soon as the Senate adjourns for the year." Again a murmur raced through the group.

An innate sense of dignity held Drew's eyes steady and his hands clasped confidently on the desk. "When we decided to marry, we knew of the odds facing us. We never dreamed that we would be hit so soon, however. The reporter in question behaved in an irresponsible manner, for which she will face the appropriate charges. Her gossip-mongering tarnishes those others of you in her profession, most of whom I know and respect.

"An injustice has been done not only to myself and my fiancée—" the title sent a thrill of excitement through Daran, whose face bore a glow of pride, "—but to Congressman Longley, with whom I have been in direct communication during this ordeal." The look he threw back at her was subtle, a promise of later explanations to satisfy her surprise at this latest discovery.

"An injustice has been done, as well, to the Honorable Rudolph Sweet, whose nomination I *will* support with my full conviction that he is a wise and able man, possessing the dignity and integrity to befit the United States Supreme Court.

"An injustice has been done to the image of government officials today, who have been so blemished by the wrongs of their predecessors that they find themselves constantly on the defensive rather than on the offensive.

"But finally, and worst, an injustice has been done to every American, whose right it is to hear and read the truth from the mouths and pens of those entrusted to seek it out." With a deep breath, he paused, looked gently back at Daran, then ended. "Thank you, ladies and gentlemen of the press. Now if you have any questions, I'd be glad to answer them, as much as it is in my ability to do so."

Amid the upshoot of hands and the buzz of voices, Daran's eyes never left Drew's tall form, standing now with studied ease, before the desk. The skill and grace with which he parried questions only enhanced the respect she felt for him. As he won over this crowd and this issue, so he had won over her heart.

Much, much later, as they lay unclothed beside each other in Drew's large bed, Daran softly questioned him. "Why ever did she do it, Drew?"

Gray eyes followed the combing of his fingers through the silk of her hair, curling over his shoulder. "For the same reason that I reacted that first day when Leo dared to put his arm around your shoulder—jealousy, pure and simple."

"Were you really jealous way back then?" she challenged in a whisper, chuckling in delight at his nod. "But what did that reporter have to be jealous of?" Her fingers intertwined with his on her rib cage.

Drew laughed gently. "That woman has been dating your ex-husband for weeks. They use each other to satisfy their own needs—it's very common in this line of work. She was particularly annoyed with his behavior later that night—she was with him in the restaurant when he saw you—and decided to take her sweet revenge." His hand snaked out to tug at her ear lobe in his own form of sweet revenge, his strong forefinger returning by way of her chin to deliver her lips up for his kiss.

When it ended, she searched the silver orbs still caressing her. "You knew all about Bill, yet you insisted I tell you. Why?" She held no anger, merely curiosity.

"Bill only told me *part* of the story; the rest I was able to piece together myself. It helped to explain that infernal

217

battle in your eyes every time I came near, much less touched you. I had to know if you trusted me enough, after everything, to still want to tell me. I'm sure—" he grinned "—that the monster in me also wanted to punish you for running off to Cleveland the way you did. I was frantic until I contacted the airlines. From now on you come to *me*, understand?" She kissed him gently, then dipped her head in agreement, before returning it to his chest.

"Even without my messages, you could have called, you know. I waited by the phone all day," Daran said.

Drew's tawny head rocked from side to side. "Not long enough. I was on your doorstep by seven, only to find the place dark and locked. All the while I believed you hadn't seen the papers, since *you* hadn't called *me*—to *my* knowledge. I had hoped to clear everything up before showing them to you. It seems Morrow jumped the gun." Daran recalled the explosion with a shudder. But Drew's pause was one of deep thought. "Actually it's my fault for what John and Leo did. With loyalty comes a tendency for overprotectiveness. They had no idea of my feelings for you; if they had, your calls would have been put through immediately. I'm afraid they did see you as the villain!" He squeezed her with his own evil taunt, then lay quiet for a moment. This was the very fullness, the wholeness which Daran cherished—this peaceful camaraderie, this fine meshing of minds. Silent with Drew, she felt complete.

"Do you know how much like your mother you are?" he murmured, his lean cheek against the crown of her head.

A smile spread over her lips as her thoughts winged to Cleveland. "She really came through for me. It's as though I've found a new friend."

Drew's chuckle tickled her ear. "She's a spitfire, that one, just like her daughter. And she loves you very much."

218

They lay still, flesh against flesh, Drew basking in Daran's warmth, she thriving on his strength. Peace and love flowed between them through the silence; soft and intermittent kisses punctuated it. Thoughts of the mad-paced day to begin within hours had no place here. There was only the moment and each other.

"What are you thinking, honey?" he whispered, his breath warm against her forehead.

"Your speech back there in the office—it was very powerful. You had them eating out of the palm of your hand at the end."

A wicked grin gleamed white in the moonlight. "That was the point. But I meant every word I said—and they knew that. Eloquence is just frosting on the cake."

As a long and sinewed arm pulled her onto her side and tucked her curves closer to his muscled length, she indulged him his cockiness. Her tongue traced tiny circles on his chest, pausing only at his sharp intake of breath. "Hmm, I could use a little of that eloquence now," she teased in husky murmur. "You know, talk of love and other such silly things . . ."

Pulling her soft body on top of his firm one, he propped her head up with his hands. "*Talk* of love? I've done enough talking today to last me a lifetime. *Action* is what we need right now!" And action was what they got. The pledges and promises had all been made; this was the time of fulfillment.

When You Want A Little More Than Romance—

Try A Candlelight Ecstasy!

Dell Bestsellers

☐ **NOBLE HOUSE** by James Clavell..............$5.95 (16483-4)
☐ **PAPER MONEY** by Adam Smith................$3.95 (16891-0)
☐ **CATHEDRAL** by Nelson De Mille...............$3.95 (11620-1)
☐ **YANKEE** by Dana Fuller Ross.....................$3.50 (19841-0)
☐ **LOVE, DAD** by Evan Hunter.......................$3.95 (14998-3)
☐ **WILD WIND WESTWARD**
  by Vanessa Royal.......................................$3.50 (19363-X)
☐ **A PERFECT STRANGER**
  by Danielle Steel...$3.50 (17221-7)
☐ **FEED YOUR KIDS RIGHT**
  by Lendon Smith, M.D. $3.50 (12706-8)
☐ **THE FOUNDING**
  by Cynthia Harrod-Eagles............................$3.50 (12677-0)
☐ **GOODBYE, DARKNESS**
  by William Manchester..................................$3.95 (13110-3)
☐ **GENESIS** by W.A. Harbinson...................$3.50 (12832-3)
☐ **FAULT LINES** by James Carroll.................$3.50 (12436-0)
☐ **MORTAL FRIENDS** by James Carroll.......$3.95 (15790-0)
☐ **THE SOLID GOLD CIRCLE**
  by Sheila Schwartz.....................................$3.50 (18156-9)
☐ **AMERICAN CAESAR**
  by William Manchester..................................$4.50 (10424-6)